The House I Built

Reflections on life,

healing, and things in between

Chris Settle

My journey in the wake of coming off a benzodiazepine
and the protracted symptoms that followed.

First paperback edition February 2022

Book design and cover concept by Chris Settle

Cover photo by Camille Settle

ISBN 978-0-578-25657-3 (paperback)

ISBN 978-0-578-25658-0 (eBook)

www.thehouseibuilt.com

To Liam, David, and Ruby.

CONTENTS

PREFACE

What this is NOT is a self-help book intended to provide expertise and guidance on how to safely rid yourself of benzos or other psychoactive drugs; rather, this is my own account of coming off a drug that wracked my brain, and the emotional challenges I faced during a slow and at times frightening healing process. In fact, if you are thinking about transitioning off these types of medications or are in the throes of recovery yourself, you may want to save this read for another day.

I thought it was important to tell my story within the context of this healing experience, to better understand how this had impacted the full arc of my life. Having said that, people often asked, "How did you continue working, despite having to deal with the issues brought on by the quick cessation of alprazolam and the protracted withdrawal that followed?" The best answer I could come up with was, "I just did." And, having had more time to contemplate the question, I'm still at a loss for a concise response. But it did ignite my curiosity. What was it that kept me going throughout this difficult time? And who am I to have survived this process which wrecks so many lives? I became determined to put it all out there, along with my own broader life strokes, to try to better understand the answers to those questions for myself.

If you know anything about the effect benzodiazepines can have on your being, you know that they're highly addictive, potentially destructive, and most certainly can be a career killer when things don't work out as intended. Which in many cases is the least of people's concerns – the one-year mortality rate for someone struggling with the effects of coming off a benzo after long-term use is around 10 percent (the data is scattered and elusive, but that's the conservative ballpark). This is serious stuff.

I don't know if the events of seven years ago and how I feel today can be directly attributed to my experience with alprazolam. In fact, several medical professionals I have worked with do not believe this to be the case. But something happened to me that left its mark. Something that changed me from that day forward, which has been at the epicenter of a healing process ever since. Which, in turn, became a central motivation for me to write this book.

INTRODUCTION

I awoke one morning to a series of events that would play out over weeks, months, and even years and leave me to wonder whether my mental faculties would ever return to normal – at least to the extent of what "normal" felt like before all this happened. Basic activities that I had grown accustomed to had now become more of a challenge. Things like how I tracked my thoughts, my sense of who I was, and my confidence were all suddenly knocked ajar. Or whether, at the age of forty-six, this marked the beginning of a slow decline in my mental health. I was desperate for answers and frightened as to what the future held.

Inspired by fear more than anything and the need to do something productive, I began to document my healing process. And felt compelled to record my more memorable life experiences. My dad's mom died in her mid-seventies of Alzheimer's, and if I were to succumb to a similar fate, although I do hold steadfast to the prodigious belief that this need not be the case, I at least wanted to get in my two cents while I still could.

I knew that the best way forward was simply to start putting words to paper and exercise my brain when all I really wanted to do was check out and bury my head under the covers. I realized that getting my thoughts down wouldn't be easy because writing isn't my strong suit, but I considered it an important enough topic to invest the time and energy and give it my best effort. I also wanted to provide my kids (and perhaps their families, one day) with an account of who I was and what I had endured during a very difficult period in my life. I wanted to leave something behind.

Before this, I had no ambition to journal my thoughts. But documenting my recovery became essential as I struggled to make sense of things. I began to record my progress in a diary, looking for trendlines to indicate patterns of healing. But it was a slow, arduous, and at times frustrating process. I eventually realized that to feel better, to come out the other side whole, I'd need to take a deeper dive into myself and change how I was living my life.

The arrangement of this book reflects the dichotomy of having to deal with a highly personal health issue while forging ahead with everyday life. The diary entries provide a linear chronicle of what I was feeling and experiencing, which was at certain times in contrast to how I presented myself in my professional and family life, as I write about in the book's narrative. This juxtaposition was essential because while my life may have appeared fine from the outside (narrative), I was struggling daily to maintain some sense of normalcy on the inside (diary). I also felt that seeing these two perspectives side by side could perhaps illuminate a deeper understanding of the value gleaned from enduring this experience. I needed to examine how I got myself into this predicament to begin with, and what I've learned about myself throughout the healing process.

I was willing to try most anything when my doctor of nearly twenty years suggested that alprazolam was the best remedy to help quiet the "mind-chatter" I was experiencing at night. It worked initially but became less effective the longer I took it. When I went back to the doctor, he added even more prescriptions and recommendations to the mix. After a few months, I realized not only were the medications he was pushing my way not working, but they were making me feel worse.

Married, with two sons and a daughter, my life had become progressively demanding. I was working at an advertising agency in a stressful role, and the company had become increasingly precarious. The adverse reactions I was now having to my medications made the prospect of losing my job that much more real. I knew I had a challenging road ahead if I wanted to remain employed.

Unfortunately, things got worse as I began to wean myself off alprazolam, and pretty much imploded when I stopped taking it altogether. I recall, the day after my last dose, a sense that something had been altered, a switch flipped. I immediately began experiencing tunnel vision, my depth perception was off, and paranoia and confusion began to creep in. A loud hissing sensation took hold in my head, and I flushed with anxiety. My focus was fuzzy, and sleep was all but impossible. My brain needed something that was no longer there.

Over time, simple tasks became overwhelming, and I struggled to get myself out the door most mornings. I was exhausted and unmotivated, and any sense of normalcy had all but left. I was now vulnerable, feeling alone and scared, and wanted to connect with someone who was going through a similar experience. I soon discovered an anonymous online chat room where people congregated in the thousands to seek answers and guidance as to why their lives had suddenly taken a turn for the worse.

As the months passed, other symptoms began to emerge. Symptoms that cast doubt on who I was as a spouse, as a father, and as an employee. I was struggling with my ability to be proactive and resolve simple life issues. It had become difficult to recall everyday things, such as what I had for breakfast and what happened the previous day, and I found it harder to engage in simple conversation. I felt disconnected from the people around me. It was like I was viewing the world through a prism, feeling spaced out as if high on paint fumes – a state of consciousness that would continue, to varying degrees, twenty-four-seven for several years.

This trial was to be a journey that – for the most part – I would have to keep to myself. To reveal too much would be to give in to its power. Insomnia and heightened anxiety, hallucinations, and many other physical and psychological indicators would conspire to derail me and keep me from living my complete self. My will and determination would be my guide as I confronted this new reality, fueled by the hope that one day I'd be well and thrive once again.

Though highly distracted and living with a considerable amount of emotional discomfort, I forged ahead, trying to remain productive and engaged with family, friends, and colleagues as best I could. My central nervous system had been jolted due to the rapid cessation of a medication that was intended to bring calm into my life. But instead, released my worst insecurities to wreak havoc on my being. I was a changed person. But, knowing I was walking a line between giving in and making the best of things, I believed my primary course of action was to roll with it until I felt better – fake it until I make it. I knew that if I gave in to this muted reality, the quality of my relationships would erode, and I wouldn't stand a chance at work.

October 1, 2013

Over the past few years, I've worked with a naturopathic doctor to help rebalance my sleep cycle. I've shown some progress lately but suspected more was going on. A reputable clinic conducted a sleep study, which determined that I had sleep apnea due to a narrow airway. Over the course of a few months, I tried various treatments – a CPAP [continuous positive airway pressure] machine and a mouth devise only increased my anxiety around sleep, leading to episodes of insomnia – if I wasn't stressed about sleep before, I had certainly become so now.

It was at about this time that my GP prescribed .5 mg of alprazolam twice a day to help take the edge off the anxiety that I was experiencing at night. Initially, I took half of the prescribed dose. Job circumstances and life issues progressively elevated my stress, culminating, in May of 2012, with the passing of my mother, at which point I increased the dose to 1 mg a night.

Over the ensuing months, it occurred to me that the drugs were having an adverse effect on my wellbeing. This became abundantly clear while attending a family gathering in early July of 2013. I was unable to take my prescription that evening, having left it back at the house, several hours' drive away. I was awakened in the early morning by a distinct hissing noise in my head and mounting anxiety. This was the first indication that something in my brain had indeed been altered to the point that it needed the medication to function properly.

Alprazolam is classified as a psychoactive drug and is part of a broader family of medications called benzodiazepines, which, unknown to me then, are very addictive and potentially detrimental to the brain. And for this reason, experts generally do not prescribe them for more than a few weeks outside of a hospital setting. Medical professionals will admit that they're not entirely sure how they work nor understand the full impact on a person's long-term health. But my doctor prescribed daily doses for about three years: long enough for my brain to adapt to its effects, rendering the medication no longer effective – and causing all sorts of adverse reactions. Not feeling well and intent on stopping the medication altogether, he and I worked up a five-week plan to rid the drug from my system. In hindsight, we grossly underestimated the time I needed to wean off safely. We should have allowed at least a year. My wife warned me of the potential effects when first prescribed, but we could not have foreseen the challenges to come.

Far too often, prescription drugs, intended to bring "calm" into our lives, suddenly backfire as we discover they don't work as expected or do more harm than good. We think we are getting the treatment we seek when we are only masking the problem, albeit temporarily. We tend to place so much faith in our care providers that we do not second guess their expertise as much as we probably should. Even something as trivial as addressing sleep, as in my case, we are putting our lives into their hands. And then, when things do not go as planned, we have little recourse to rectify the damage incurred. And, if things do go sideways after deciding to go off these medications, it's nothing to be ashamed of – except for those responsible for unleashing them into our lives in the first place, ignorant of the protocols necessary to accommodate each person's unique circumstances and sensitivities.

Footnote. It's come to my attention that the phrase "Slept with Camille," present in several diary entries throughout, can mean different things. So, not to confuse the reader, I thought it helpful to clarify its meaning within the context as I intended – to be in a state of sleep. During much of my post-benzo recovery period, my anxiety levels were so high that I could not tolerate sharing my bed with another person, notably my wife.

ONE

THE FORMATIVE YEARS

I was born in a sanitarium in Hinsdale, Illinois on January 18, 1967, just outside of my hometown of Western Springs (fig. 1, p. 188).

November 2, Day One

Today marks the beginning of my new self. I had been experiencing manageable issues with sleep, anxiety, and a lack of focus. But on this day, things have taken a turn for the worse. I will track the healing progress following the cessation of alprazolam and record everything that happens.

Not that a sanitarium was medically necessary; it just happened to have the closest birthing facility to our home. It was the back-up plan in the event I came out sooner than expected. I'd done a fair amount of lounging around in the breech position and apparently decided one evening to "right" myself, which mom took as a sign to pack her bags. A couple spoonfuls of castor oil and I was out in a few hours.

The youngest of three, I grew up in a tight-knit community about twenty miles west of Chicago. My nearest sibling, Scott, was about three and half years older than me, and Kent was eighteen months his senior (fig. 2, p. 188). Since I was a few years younger than them, I tended to be more of a tagalong. However, Scott and I did enjoy many of the same things, such as playing with Matchbox cars, Legos, and Lincoln Logs. He and I had more things in common than I did with Kent (probably because we were closer in age), who generally kept to himself – he was more reserved and introspective. Scott was a big kid; according to our mom overtook Kent in size around the age of three. As he neared his teens, Scott got more temperamental, and sometimes the consequences weren't to my advantage. But fortunately, he never punched above the neckline, and although tumultuous at times, we did get along more often than not and somehow survived those formative years intact.

Western Springs was a township landlocked by forest reserves, urban sprawl, and a tangled network of freeways and railroad tracks. It was a safe and picturesque town with lots to do in a relatively compact space. It had a community swimming pool, a few spacious parks, and a five-and-dime all within a convenient stroll from home. Aside from the train whistles and the blast of an occasional weather siren, it was a quiet town. An oasis comprised of mostly White, middle-class conservatives, living out their lives, indifferent to the inequities just twenty minutes to the east. At one point we had dozens of kids living on our block, which made for endless hours of outdoor fun. Around every corner, in every backyard or alley, there was always something to do: an adventure waiting to be discovered. Western Springs was the perfect place to be a kid.

When I was little, I was very active and had a hard time sitting still. This is ironic because I turned out to be a low-key person – less outspoken, more introspective, and thoughtful. Which is what my future wife would apparently find interesting in me one day (go figure). I also had an early knack for painting and drawing, showing my artwork at the local library by the age of seven, earning notoriety from my classmates and teachers as the "artistic kid" (fig. 3, p. 188). The contemplative side I got from my dad, my "determination" from my mom, and my creative sensibilities from both, with a lot of me sprinkled in to fill the rest.

Mom was one of the hardest-working people I've known. She would put 100 percent into everything she touched, always busy with projects around the house: repairing, updating, sprucing and arranging. She also loved to entertain family and friends with fancy meals, spending all day in the kitchen planning, cooking, chopping, and basting. Checking off those projects one by one, burning herself down to the wick, she pushed herself to her limits. Somehow, she found the energy to maintain the house, raise three boys, experiment with art, and hold down a job later in life to see her kids through their respective colleges.

She was driven to do twice the work so that others would benefit. It was not enough for her to paint a room; she'd take on an entire house, floor to ceiling, meticulously updating the color scheme and furnishings to satisfy that sense of home that she envisioned for her family. She liked things to look a certain way – almost dreamlike. She infused a bit of herself into everything through color choice and design. She'd do the work often relegated to a hired hand, adding to the family coffers through hard-earned sweat-equity. It makes sense to me now that her children have a similar need to take on projects many might consider too daunting to do themselves – landscaping a yard, putting up a fence, or building a house. But this was instilled in us as part of our early training. It would be our cross to bear.

Mom is the reason we had joy in our lives. She had a positive energy about her, and it was felt by everyone. In her presence, you were captivated by her empathetic and authentic nature. And it made no difference whether they were family, friends, or strangers; she was welcoming to everyone. She cared about what you had to say and could talk endlessly and substantively about most anything, punctuated by an effortless laugh that resonated from the center of her being. Her aura was magical. It made you feel safe and believe that the world was a much better place than it really was when in her presence.

When I was a little, she would tend to my bumps and bruises

with such kindness (fig. 4, p. 188). I cherish the memories of how she would pick me up and rock me in her arms and her gentle words of comfort. Long into my adulthood, she'd still be there to see me through those rough patches. She could illuminate the gloomier days with her smile and infectious optimism and lighten whatever burden may have befallen me that day. She was a warrior and a worrier, and she epitomized what it meant to be there for someone when they needed it most.

My dad wasn't around much. He traveled a lot for his job domestically. Even though we lived in the Midwest, he worked for the New York Times as a photojournalist (fig. 5, p. 188). This centrally located post enabled him to cover important stories throughout the Midwestern states: events that were happening in and around the region during the late sixties and seventies – the Vietnam war protests, human rights demonstrations, political upheaval, and other defining moments of the era. I didn't really miss him at the time – it was just the way things were – and yet his absence created distance between us, and no doubt, must have taken a toll on the marriage. Raising three boys was more than enough of a task for two, and much of that responsibility fell to Mom.

Dad was a sensitive, introverted artist who saw the world differently than most. He was an only child, and his parents put a lot of emphasis on image and discipline over nurturing and wellbeing. He was the son of an accountant and a housewife, raised with conservative values in a small, middle-class town in the heart of Kansas. His childhood was somewhat sheltered, and he kept to himself a lot. This solitary upbringing and quiet nature made it more difficult for him to connect with people and express his feelings.

He could be critical too, and I think that left an imprint on me. Being the youngest, with a three-and-a-half-year gap between my nearest sibling, I could be a handful for sure. And I suspect some of those marital tensions may have bled my way, especially after I began to walk and talk and push back.

Maybe it was because of how I reacted to things, but I felt like a bit of an outcast. Dad responded angrily to lots of the little things I'd do, with a "don't do that … get off this … stop touching that!" along with a look of disdain, followed by the occasional slap or, more often, a well-earned spanking. He was loving in many ways but not very patient when his kids acted out. However, it was this critical feedback that left me feeling frustrated. And wondering whether I would ever measure up or be good enough. Kent and Scott didn't seem to experience the same reactions as often, nor do I believe did they internalize dad's irritation as I did. But I'm sure they felt it in other ways.

Luckily, I realized at an early age that dads' reactions toward me were more out of frustration than how he felt deep down. More so, I perceived his behavior to be a reflection of the way his father must have treated him. I think this wisdom was my saving grace and one of the dividends of my intuitive side.

Nevertheless, later in life, this early conditioning began to re-emerge as self-doubt. I found myself second-guessing my own talents and abilities, more averse to taking on new things. Eventually, I found the work I did to be less and less fulfilling. That inner voice nullified my sense of purpose, questioning my self-worth, discrediting my efforts, and distracting me from life's invitations to grow. I became my own worst critic. Was this a direct result of those early influences? It's hard to say. Maybe it's just a part of who I am. But it begs the question of how much impact we do have on our kids.

November 6, Year One

I developed a dependency on alprazolam due to long-term use. .5mg for about three years taken periodically and 1 mg nightly for the past year or so. In addition, I have been prescribed 10 mg of zaleplon nightly for the past three months and 100mg of valerian root nightly for nine weeks. All recommended and prescribed by my doctor.

I began a drawdown of all three medications in early October. I achieved initial success omitting valerian and zaleplon within three weeks. I completed the alprazolam drawdown under the supervision of my doctor on November 2, last dose of .25mg, according to the following schedule: .5mg for two weeks, .375 for seven days, .25mg for another week, and stopping dosage altogether at the end of that time frame. In hindsight, this was too rapid and was consequently harmful to my nervous system.

I'm currently experiencing extreme rebound insomnia with no sleep the first two nights and two- or three-hours' sleep on the third night. Tracking daily mood and sleep performance – cognitive function improving despite lack of sleep. Coping with anxiety and mood swings including mild depression.

Showing day-over-day incremental improvement, overall feeling optimistic. Eating well, drinking plenty of fluids, sticking to an exercise program, and sleep schedule as best I can. Maintaining a full-time workweek thus far and relatively normal home life. Sleeping separately from Camille for now, receiving her full support. Research says that this kind of reaction after ceasing the drug is not uncommon and improvement should follow within three to four days as the GABA center [the main inhibitory neurotransmitter in the brain] begins to regain its natural function and progressively improve over a few weeks or longer. The immediate plan is to stay the course.

Coincidentally, just finished a two-month program on Mindfulness-Based Stress Reduction (MBSR).

I feel a palpable inner tension when creating art. Sometimes I'll catch myself wondering whether the result will be satisfactory and getting frustrated when I think it should be better. These feelings and my reactions to them are most likely a carry-over from those early interactions; highlighting mistakes over successes, telling me to "stop" more than to "do," vocalizing dissatisfaction over reward.

Part of the responsibility of being a parent is to cultivate enough awareness to understand the power our reactive side can have over our children and have the maturity to reel it in when it matters most. Admittedly, this is a work in progress for me. I've never lashed out physically, but my tongue has been prone to leave the barn on occasion.

With age and earned perspective, I now better understand the benefits of refocusing my intentions towards the act of doing, rather than on the result – because … can it ever really be good enough? I have freed myself of the perception that it is the outcome that matters most, which is stoked by an upbringing and culture that places such high regard on achievement. To become "worthy" means you must be the "best" at something or don't even bother trying. Sure, it's nice to be proficient, but it's not everything.

November 11, Year One, Email

Hi Dr. Ng, I'm coming up on ten days since my final dose of alprazolam. Experiencing intermittent bouts of anxiety throughout the day, more pronounced in the evenings, makes sleep very difficult. I'm struggling and want to know what's next.

While growing up in Western Springs, summer brought our family together in exceptionally close proximity. Every year, like clockwork, the five of us would pack ourselves into our little yellow camper, intent on crisscrossing the continent in pursuit of some National Park, monument, or long-lost relative.

I recall mile after mile, the drone of the road reverberating from beneath the tires. And the sound of the snapping and popping of the curtains as the wind rattled through the screens. I also remember the smell of our musty old canvas tent (fig. 6, p. 188) and being told to put that stick back in the fire a hundred times. Those hot, muggy nights, lying awake on a bone-crushing air mattress. The mosquitoes buzzing around my ears; long walks schlepping to landmarks I could have cared less about. And the countless steps and backtracking to take the perfect family photo.

After a day frolicking on the beach and a sleepless night tossing and turning, trying to avoid patches of sunburn, we headed off to the Kennedy Space Center in our trusty camper to witness the launch of the last of the great Saturn V rockets. My family and I, along with thousands of onlookers, filed onto a slim strip of land to stake a claim. We set up our blankets and camping chairs and settled in for the long wait. After a couple of hours enduring the sweltering heat, an announcement came over the loudspeakers: "All systems go … T minus ten, nine …" Tensions were high, and everyone fell silent. Within moments, a puff of blue smoke appeared across the bay but no sound; how odd, I thought. Then, the spectacle of an explosion: a plume quickly formed, followed seconds later by a thunderous rumble. The ground pounded as if a tree had been felled right next to us. The vibrations were so strong, I thought my body was going to shake apart. I could see people screaming jubilantly but heard nothing coming out of their mouths. The giant cloud then began to lift the lipstick-shaped container arduously up into the sky. The rocket with its immense payload (the Skylab space station) began to accelerate and, to my astonishment, was out of sight within minutes. That day my imagination was transported to a whole other level. I fell in love with the stars and became mesmerized with their origin and their relationship to our own existence.

The camper ecosystem was ripe for family strife. And I, being the pain that I could be, was quick to irritate others when agitated – or just because. I could be mouthy and irreverent, which kept family vacation bliss in check. Nevertheless, these trips were a summer ritual and the highlight of my younger years. I am grateful to my dad for taking us on these adventures and for my mom's Herculean efforts to make it all happen. Cramming everything a family of five could possibly need, and then some, into a tenement on wheels to sustain life on the road for weeks at a time. These memories, though seemingly torturous at times (with all the schlepping, photo retakes, and – yes – the occasional family quarrel), lay the groundwork for what I aspired to achieve one day with my own family. I wouldn't trade them for the world.

Between the vacations, holidays, those famous grilled-cheese hot dog sandwiches, cub scouts, and Indian guides (fig. 7, p. 188) ... Dad sought ways to be with his kids and show his love for his family. It was a challenge for him to fit it all in. It always is. I know his learning curve was steep, but he did his best and made it work.

We give our parents so much grief because we expect so much of them. The older we get, and the less friendly the world around us may seem, we tend to blame them for not doing enough to make everything perfect, for not infusing eternal happiness into our lives. Only when we have had a chance to walk in their shoes and experience firsthand the challenges they faced, we contemplate the effect all that tension and rebellion must have had on them. As children, pushing against the rules, doing and saying reckless things, our behavior is destined to result in arguments and an erosion of trust. For some reason, this must be the way of young people: the natural foray into one's own carving out of independence. And for us parents, it's an opportunity to accept things as they are meant to be, whether they fit the plan or not.

November 14, Year One

I set in motion a two-week plan to work half-time at home and spend more time on myself – meditating and eating right. I informed my office of the situation, and they were very supportive.

Note to work: I need to bow out of the Phoenix trip. The process of recovering from the effects of a medication I recently stopped is likely to take several more weeks. I'll be functioning in a fog for a while and can be most productive if I stay behind to focus on project work. Your flexibility and understanding are greatly appreciated. Please cancel my flight and hotel room.

A bit more info if you're interested:

Xanax is a commonly prescribed medication intended to help offset the effects of anxiety. But it is also used to help people fall asleep. Its generic form is called alprazolam. A portion of people coming off the medicine experience withdrawal symptoms much greater than the initial issue it was intended to serve – and I seem to fall into this category. In my case, it's wreaking havoc on my sleep. These symptoms are temporary but require time to run their course.

Thanks, I'll keep you posted as this moves along.

At night during the summer, the neighborhood kids would often gather for a game of kick-the-can. To select teams, we'd rely on a shortlist of rhymes. Among the options was "Eeny, meeny, miny, moe, catch a n*gger by the toe ... what color was the blood?" We didn't know what it meant; we just liked its catchy phrasing and functional utility – something one of the older kids must have picked up at the dinner table. However, to be "it" meant you were the one selected to do all the chasing and, as far as I was concerned, it was much more fun to be the one getting chased, running, and hiding, blending in with the shadows, evading capture, than to be the one in pursuit.

To be "it" also meant being relegated to the role of prison guard, staked out in front of the jail (front porch), and responsible for capturing all the "escapees," which involved an awful lot of searching, seeking, and waiting. To be "seen," chased down, then tagged meant you were caught. And on rare occasions, we'd experience the satisfaction of someone kicking the can, usually a discarded soda can, which meant freeing the jail and releasing everyone back into the darkness to hide once again, essentially resetting the game. To hear the crack of the can as it was struck was beyond exhilarating and yet bittersweet. These sagas often lasted several hours, which meant freeing the jail could signal the end of the game, at which point it would be time for us all to go home. One of those nights ended prematurely for me when I collided with a friend while jumping through a hedge, breaking my leg in two places below the knee (fig. 8, p. 188).

Winters in Chicago were as cold as you'd expect, forcing many of us to hunker down indoors for days on end in search of other activities and things to do. Depending on the mood of the rabbit-ears, we maybe had a handful of channels, mostly soap operas during the day and a few newscasts in the evenings – followed by episodes of Andy Griffith at dinner, then Flip Wilson, capped off with Carol Burnett before bedtime. When we did venture outside, we'd head off to Spring Rock Park for an afternoon of ice skating to test the strength of our ankles in garage-sale floppy leather skates. To stay warm, we'd gather around the circular stone fire pit, watching the plumes of steam rise from our frozen feet propped up along its edge. And dry our mittens, careful not to stack them too close to the flames.

November 16, Year One

If there was a looming thought or worry it would be "lack of sleep." But I remind myself that what I'm experiencing is temporary and is part of the healing process. I must accept this. My focus will simply be about relaxation in the moment – anxious thoughts must travel through, are fleeting, and will lessen over time.

I had quite a few friends when I was little and we liked to play in the dirt and climb trees, collecting the usual bumps and scrapes. I was an early bloomer, taller than the rest, and mostly gentle – but I did lash out on occasion if someone irritated me. I think this was due to some of those frustrations from home bubbling up to the surface. But as I got older, as is the way of things, my interests would soon progress to other, more important subjects.

I met this girl in the fifth grade. She was new to the area and had started the school year a couple of weeks late. She lived a few blocks away from us with her mom and older sister and a picture of Eric Idle (from Monty Python) hung on the kitchen wall – the topic came up once or twice; her aunt was dating him or something. I didn't really pay much attention to Kristen at first, but within a short while I noticed something unusual about her – she liked me.

She too was more mature in appearance. Blonde and blue-eyed, and tall as well. She had a glow about her that made me feel funny – the way she looked at me, her smile. I didn't understand it at the time, but I liked being around her too. We spent hours on the phone. Me in my bed, looping my finger around the cord nervously, while she listened and laughed on the other end. We began to hang out after school, which soon progressed into intoxicating moments of hand-holding. I was captivated.

The old Ford sedan was parked off to the side, just out of sight, abutted against the back of our garage. The forties-era car had been sitting so long that the tires were flat, and the paint had earned its fair share of weathering, otherwise, the car was pristine in appearance. In our minds, it served no other purpose than to be a gathering place for the few of us looking for something to do, and to be alone.

The windows were frosted over, softening the light as it made its way into the cavernous interior, freezing the moments on the inside, recording our presence – the perfect hideaway, where time had no purpose and nothing else mattered. Where the first sparks of love were etched into our hearts, to mark the beginning of what it meant to acknowledge a person in this way. Her lips, the flush of her cheeks, the pink tip of her nose. The jolt that rattled through my body as we nestled together to say warm.

And when Kristen finally kissed my cheek, it was then she left her mark. An imprint for all to follow – the bar had been set, its lure cast. An unquenchable desire was set in motion, a force that would challenge my relationships henceforth. An ache that would haunt me for years. Somewhere, deep inside, a switch had been tripped, a failsafe mechanism to ensure procreation. It cannot be contained, is unattainable, and can lead some astray or even to go mad. It's real and at the same time false.

Some forty years later, by pure chance, I reconnected with an old friend online from the neighborhood, Kate, who just happened to be present one of those afternoons. She was a classmate who lived directly behind us, and the car had once belonged to her grandfather. She'd stake out the front seat with our friend Bryce, while Kristen and I hung out in the back. It was innocent, we were just kids, but no less potent. Without much preamble, short of "It's been a while, how's it going?" She told the story in her own words. "Remember the time in that old car behind my house?"

November 20, Year One

Tried to sleep with Camille last night and got anxious. Managed to drift off after she agreed to move out of the room. Too soon.

Met with my naturopathic and got some B vitamins. She indicated that I should continue to improve over the next few weeks.

That magical winter ended abruptly for me though when my dad got reassigned to the New York office. And just like that, my family and I were headed to a different life. Needless to say, I was crushed. Kristen and I exchanged letters for a couple of years, but they eventually trailed off. However, the impact she had on me only grew with intensity, and the memories of those moments shared were emblazoned on my soul forevermore.

November 21, Year One

I slept poorly last night – maybe three or four hours. Was restless despite taking 125 mg of trazodone.

Will go to work for a few hours today to see how the day goes.

When we arrived at our new home in Montclair, New Jersey, we were pressed for time. We only had about a week to get settled in before Christmas and to prepare for school. However, a few days after unloading our things, we got hit by a ten-year blizzard which shut down the city and tacked an additional week onto the winter break. Fortunately, our new backyard was long and sloped, which made for the perfect toboggan run, with twists and turns and a spine-jarring jump at the bottom (fig. 9, p. 189). Frozen fingers and toes made me feel right at home, albeit temporarily.

I entered the fifth grade in the middle of the year and didn't know a soul. The school district had recently been desegregated and we resided in a neighborhood adjacent to a deprived urban area. No buffer this time, no railroad tracks; we were separated only by a few city blocks and the privilege of living on the hill.

Most of the kids in our immediate neighborhood were from affluent families and able to maintain their status at their chosen private schools, but my brothers and I were re-assigned to what up to this point had been predominantly "Black schools" within the public school system. We were now a part of the newly formed patchwork of students from disparate neighborhoods cobbled together to once and for all show the country that Black and White students could and should interact side-by-side. And with this, for the first time, I experienced a level of insecurity that I had never felt before. The adjustment was difficult, and I struggled to fit in. Apparently, it was up to our generation to make right what those before us couldn't seem to figure out. To be a "them" was eye-opening.

For the most part, the kids were welcoming, but there was nominal oversight and a clear lack of commitment from many of the students. This was a minimally funded school with many kids coming from broken families with little means. Some were sent there simply as a diversion from the temptations beckoning them to a life on the streets. Regardless of intentions, everyone was competing for attention, and we were all drawing down what little resources were available. Whatever problems I was facing, theirs were far more significant.

I was an outsider, with no friends. I was tall and gangly and, of course, I stood out. And with this came a significant amount of bullying – from name-calling to shoving, and many invitations to get my ass kicked. I wasn't looking for trouble though; I was too distracted mourning the loss of my friends back home – I missed them, especially Kristen. In the beginning, I was functioning in survival mode, miserable and unable to do much about it except lay low, stay the course, and somehow get to the end of each day with all my teeth. I did eventually make a few friends.

I had my lunch physically taken from me on more than one occasion. He felt kind of bad about it. I could see it in his face. However, oddly enough, I didn't feel like a victim. I felt empathy; I could see myself doing the same thing if I were in his situation – hungry, with no means to buy lunch. And I recall looking forward to a day when we didn't have to manage through such inequity. Thinking that all we needed was a few more years to iron out these differences so the next generation wouldn't have to experience the indignity of having to assault someone to eat, especially at school. I mean, wasn't that the point of all this – to balance out the playing field?

I entered middle school as a sixth grader. It was a large school compared to what I was used to. And the kids drifted in and out with little purpose. The teachers didn't help matters attending to those who showed little interest in learning yet swallowed up a lot of the class time; it was all they could do to maintain order. The assignments weren't challenging, the standards were low, and the staff was spread way too thin to pay much attention to individuals who wanted to better themselves. And it wasn't uncommon to see a student get his face kicked in at recess, fistfights in the hallway, or an arrest over the confiscation of a gun or drugs found during a random locker check. It was all new to me. And yet an everyday occurrence for the kids who grew up in this part of the city. And for their parents too, I'm sure. And unfortunately, it seems, for generations to come, leaving me to wonder today whether an equitable society will ever be attainable.

The process of integrating the schools was long overdue – and we just happened to be caught at the tail end of the initial rollout. Societal baggage and governmental oppression were all laid bare and dumped on unsuspecting students and teachers to try and sort out on their own. It was a loosely conceived attempt to integrate communities that had long been systematically divided by economic and social inequality. I began to slip behind academically. And soon formed habits that made it hard for me to thrive over the ensuing years.

I didn't realize it then but having gone through this experience, seeing the challenges minorities face firsthand was one of the best educations I could have had.

November 25, Year One

Slept about seven hours – great for a Sunday night!

All I can do is think positively and remind myself that this is a healing process and will take time. I've made progress, and yet more is to be made.

As a kid, I tried a lot of different sports and did have some athletic ability. I was relatively fast, coordinated for a tall guy, and fairly strong. It was fun to participate, but I lost interest when the coaches started yelling, calling out my faults, and pushing me to do better

– I perceived their feedback as criticism, which didn't sit well with me. I liked to compete but could become discouraged when told what to do, especially when I wasn't getting the results I wanted.

I didn't participate in a sport long enough to reap the rewards it could bring. I think I disliked being "average" so much that I'd use it as an excuse not to invest myself fully. I tended to expect to be good at something right away. I thought, why put in the effort if it didn't come easily? To "win," in my mind, wasn't that big of a deal – but to look bad was everything, and therefore not worth the risk of failure and feeling embarrassed in front of my peers. If it didn't come naturally, even more reason not to pursue it.

Short of a few friendly pick-up games on weekends, I never had much desire to play baseball, let alone watch it. I think the early clincher was when one of the neighborhood kids took a line drive to the face. I'd never seen so much blood. Golf would be a close second. I had little interest in anything that involved making contact with a ball. Soccer would be no exception, and I sampled organized football only briefly when I was ten. A futile attempt to emulate the fun I once had playing "smear the queer" with my brothers and friends in our backyards. A game in which two sides are chosen and a ball is tossed from one side to the other and retrieved by a brave participant who then finds themselves on the receiving end of an all-out pile on by the players from the other team (fig. 10, p. 189). I guess the thinking was that if you were dumb enough to catch the ball, that made you the queer. However, I did participate in individual sports like track, wrestling, a little swimming (fig. 11, p. 189), and distance running. Something about having the coach off my back and others less reliant on me for their success made things more enjoyable, and I also liked the freedom to explore at my own pace.

November 26, Year One

Full day at work – progressively more anxious. I am frustrated at the realization that this has once again emerged.

Worrying about how long this might take and whether I can sustain this for another month, let alone two. I pray for wellness and healing. Scares me to think that this could be permanent.

In addition to my artistic side, I have some musical sensibilities. I can feel a song and express it through tapping. I took piano lessons for a few years but was too antsy and undisciplined to stick with it. Instead, I followed my dad's lead and took up the drums. I became technically proficient and enjoyed connecting the beat to the music but had difficulty getting in and out of songs on cue. It's like I could do the hard stuff but just didn't know how to get on and off the train when it mattered most. My sense of rhythm was fine, but my recall of song dynamics, lyrics, and timing sucked.

Drumming requires the whole body to work in unison to keep time and facilitate the many different aspects of the instrument – it suits my fidgety side well. It's challenging yet satisfying, combining the elements. One foot up, the other down, pulling it all together with one hand, dropping in accents with the other – to form complex patterns. But to fully buy into the discipline would have required me to overcome the timing hurdles that felt counterintuitive to my musical side. I thought if I had the "gift," if it just came naturally, I would have thrived. A familiar excuse. Who knows? I'm not dead yet. My wife has these gifts. It's not fair.

November 30, Year One

The past couple of days have brought bouts of depression, sadness, and some depersonalization – like I'm functioning outside of myself. The anxiety does seem less sharp compared with weeks past, but it modulates in and out. The most present symptoms would be ringing in the ears and fuzzy-headedness.

TWO
....

THOUGHTS ON RACE

Maybe it is the way I was raised. But when I see a person of color, I see color. Am I what is wrong with society? I appreciate a person's immediate, beautiful, and unique qualities and cannot help but wonder about their back story and where they came from. And find it intriguing when I meet people whose ethnicity differs from mine or who clearly come from a different part of the world.

The telling of the American Revolution fixates on one type of outcome as if it somehow exonerates White people from having to acknowledge racism from within themselves. As if this country somehow did African Americans a favor by simply affording them the tiniest margin of a seat at the table. When, in fact, it only marked the beginning of the much more arduous task of having to sort out what it means to afford liberties and freedoms to everyone. Rules interpreted by mostly White male legislators reluctant to give an inch to anyone who dares threaten their way of life – despite language that promises inalienable rights for all. Laws wrote to provide access to things, ideas, and opportunities for each citizen. And yet here we are today, still wrestling with the notion of what "equality for all" really means, or at least how to apply it fully as intended.

I see some victimized by the broader narrative, squandering what few opportunities do happen their way, using historical baggage as a barrier to moving forward. "I was this therefore I can't be that." I suppose you can't experience oppression to any degree without being victimized to some extent. And to me, that is much more reason to marvel at those who did find a way to overcome and make a difference, despite whatever challenges they may have faced. However, these exceptions do not mean it is fair. Just because a person has somehow realized their full potential does not mean everyone has access to the same opportunities. Inspiring stories should be more commonplace, less exceptional, and not touted as evidence that injustices have been fully rectified. But I do believe that if you add enough feathers to the pile, it will eventually tip the scale. And I look forward to a day when we can treat our differences respectfully, with the dignity and acceptance everyone deserves.

I think minorities make for better people and are even more intelligent in some ways – especially those for whom English is their second language. I say "better" because many first-generation immigrants are living examples of what can be overcome when confronted with adverse and challenging circumstances, such as having to relocate their families due to homeland strife in pursuit of a better way of life. People must be embraced and welcomed, not shoved aside and oppressed. Their experience is a gift in waiting for those who may one day benefit from their support and understanding. It broadens our worldview and enriches our community.

Rather than shying away from the world, we need to adapt and move forward. We need to recognize and accept our cultural differences and the confluences that brought us together, and we need to teach these lessons of resilience and inclusion to our children.

This isn't about race. It is about humanity's inert drive to push out the unfamiliar or extinguish it altogether. In those early days the West had certain wealth and advantages: there just happened to be more of "us" than "them", and we just happened to have better weapons – and we leveraged those strengths to gain the upper hand. And unfortunately, that is what happens between humans, men in particular, when they feel threatened – they wield their power over others. To change our laws, we need to change our humanity – and apparently, this takes a while.

Despite the despicable acts we've seen captured on bodycams

and cell phones, the adversity minorities face nowadays is in no small part fueled by inaccessibility to basic needs. Its effect, subjugation by a thousand obstacles. A less egregious form of abuse, nevertheless with outcomes no less oppressive. A product of a system of biases and rules built into our cultural ideology leaving many at a disadvantage. Thirty-eight years after that kid took my lunch, others facing similar circumstances still can't get enough to eat.

None of us are immune to racial bias, regardless of our upbringing. And I can say, with a tinge of irony, that the most fear-laden moments of my life haven't involved the Black guy in the dark alley scenario – well, maybe one. Such as the morning I was flanked by two suspicious-looking White guys while crossing the street on the way to my office. Or the drug-crazed hippie who smacked his girlfriend and dragged her across the grass by her hair. And the night I witnessed a Black man beaten to near incoherence and stuffed into the trunk of a car. Or when the leader of the "free world" casually asserted there were "very fine people on both sides." My fear is not of minorities. It is for minorities.

I've been around many people who come from different parts of the world, and I struggle to see what's remotely scary about that. Fear's not what people think it is. It is of our own making. There is an evolutionary aspect of fear to protect us from real threats, but in the modern world, most of it is counterintuitive to the act of giving more of oneself so that others may benefit.

I don't keep a tally of my culturally diverse friends – I only have a few "friends" as it is. But I am appalled by the thought of inequality imposed on any one of them. Simply because of who they are. I always have been. Maybe it *was* how I was raised. We carry a big responsibility as parents.

I may personally be well-intentioned, but as I've gotten older, I see that I haven't done enough for those who are still feeling and living the effects of oppression at any level. In fact, I believe these insights give me a heightened responsibility to be part of the solution rather than living out an insular life as a member of the White

majority. I put this into practice as best I can, in the way I interact with others in my profession, how I greet people on the street,
and in other day-to-day social settings and interactions, but there's
much more to be done. Real change must happen at the human
level, not simply within the legal system – the two must go together.
Whoever you are, I am intrigued by your story, and I believe that
everyone deserves the same chance as everybody else. I'm trying
harder to do my part.

December 3, Year One

*Fear of the future and guilt about not sleeping with Camille are the
causes of most stress and depression at this time. I must have faith
that I will continue to heal and remind myself not to worry about
the future.*

*Forgetfulness and spaciness bother me, and my cognitive processes
are still diminished. Some of this could be the side effects of trazodone. Will have to see.*

THREE
....

THE HIGH SCHOOL YEARS

About a year after we arrived on the East Coast, the New York Times went on strike, and dad found himself out of work, with no end in sight. Mom rationed our lunches as best she could. But after a few months, it became clear dad needed to find a new job. A national search led to The Philadelphia Inquirer and The Seattle Times as his best prospects, Seattle edging out slightly due to higher pay. Once again, we were headed on a plane to start anew, and thank God because I wasn't sure how much longer we were going to last. After we arrived in Seattle, I finished out the sixth grade and my relatively uneventful middle school years, and then off to high school I went.

These four years were marked by close calls, dark moods, crazy, and often reckless encounters. We were bystanders tossed into a mix of rules and protocols intended to turn us into quality citizens one day. There were exceptions, the focused few, but they didn't hang out in my circle. I cringe when I think back on these times.

Those crystal blue eyes were like grappling hooks, and she had a smile that could suck the air out of a room. But she wasn't interested in the fantasy I'd cooked up in my head (something about living out our lives in the back seat of an old sedan), so we became friends. Nevertheless, this left me feeling "unlovable" as I grew desperate to fill the void I left behind in Chicago. "Something must be wrong with me" would become a recurring theme in moments of doubt. In the years we knew each other, there was mutual interest, and at times infatuation, but we were worlds apart. The amount of time I spent dwelling on the thought of what could be eventually helped me realize how much emphasis I was placing on others to try and bridge my unfulfilled gaps. I needed something or someone outside of myself to make me feel good, and that's never a good thing.

December 4, Year One

Two weeks ago, I couldn't work a full day. Two weeks from today, I'll be feeling even that much better!

[From this day forward, I began to track data related to my symptoms and how I felt so I could monitor and measure my progress over time. I came up with a rating system between 0 and 10, where ten was very bad (intolerable – a ten meant that I'd go mad or be dead). And 0 equated to no symptoms at all. I split my symptoms up into four categories: anxiety, mood,

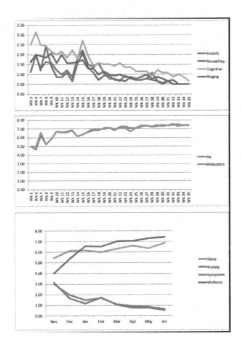

and depression, cognitive, and ringing in the ears and head. The second group of data I called "wellness." And this included tracking information related to joy and motivation. The rating of 8 meant that I felt "optimal" in those areas – optimal compared to my own life experience, not some aspirational idea of what I thought optimal should be. These summed up the areas of concern that were most meaningful to me. I also recorded my sleep patterns. I continued this for thirty-five weeks, at which point my progress stalled, and my naturopathic doctor suggested I ease off the tracking, so I didn't become completely obsessed.]

Getting a license at sixteen used to be a big deal. But today, with all the ride apps, transportation options, and parents willing to pick up and drop off their kids anywhere at a moment's notice, this ritual is far less significant than it once was. For me, it was a 1964 Ford Falcon that opened up my social network. It was a gift from my grandmother, Doris, in the late summer of '82. She drove to church daily and to and from the store on occasion. She even got a ticket once for going forty-five on the freeway. Despite Kent nearly trashing it driving eighteen hundred miles from Hutchinson to Seattle, it was in remarkable condition. If ever there was a "grandma car," this was it. Minus the late-stage stress test over three mountain passes.

The Falcon was a hip car with that vintage look. I cherished it, fixed it up, and made it my own: a process that taught me responsibility and pride of ownership. Mechanically, it was a collection of metal parts that needed constant coaxing to stay in motion (fig. 12, p. 189). Within a couple of months, I added wide tires, custom rims, and a coat of dark-gray metallic paint from the money I'd earned painting houses over the summer.

After a couple of years of jump-starts and mounting expenses, I swapped out the Falcon for a '69 Bug, which I bought from the parents of a classmate during my senior year for $750. That was a hip car too, and it had to endure two engine rebuilds to keep it in motion as well. It withstood a marathon road trip to the Midwest and eventually saw me through college. I fixed it up to its original luster and sold it shortly after I met Camille for almost four times what I paid.

It's interesting how these inanimate containers encompass so much meaning – loyal companions, witness to many of our early experiences. Subjected to hours of sing-alongs, arguments, and stray french fries. Struck by fists and yet never hitting back, their cables and pads saving your hide more than once. I think of them fondly. Long-lost friends who, if they could, would add even more detail to those spotty memories – and maybe even set a few things straight. Cocoons that protected us through countless situations in which things could have just as easily gone wrong. But we survived – most of us anyway. I look back with gratitude – and I'll be damned if I'll allow any kid of mine to partake in that kind of behavior! "Here, let me drive instead."

These were different times. No cell phones, more autonomy, less perceived risk. A sense that the natural order of things was to get out there and explore the environment with minimal oversight and retribution, even if you did get caught doing whatever it was you weren't supposed to be doing. These years offered remnants of a mystery that I can only imagine our forebears had as they too made their way into unknown territories. Driven by that thirst for adventure, life's invitation to step out and explore, uncertain of what lies in wait – the only barrier to discovery is lack of imagination (or a set of wheels).

Nowadays, with the internet, social media, and all the rules that have been put in place (no thanks to my generation's mishaps, I'm sure), our kids are left with fewer opportunities to explore and learn. Even if it's not the parents imposing these constraints, society, modernization, and instant access to answers to "what ifs" collude to dissuade our children from seeking out what lurks around their own corners. What's the point if everything discoverable is available at your fingertips, and everything else is too dangerous to even try?

And more often, that "danger" becomes the draw for the adventure-seeking kid – able and willing to push the boundaries and venture outside the "safe zone" for the fulfillment, choosing to indulge in extreme sports and other high-risk activities. My eldest, Liam, is no exception, scaling bridges and cranes to satisfy his own wild side. Opting for a motorcycle over the safe confines of a car – how dare he skip that rite of passage! Testing our will as parents and compelling us to impose rules and ultimatums to retain our own sanity. Activities once considered unthinkable to us, climbing to death-defying heights, or flinging oneself off cliffs, are all too tempting an outlet for these frontier-seeking souls defiant of a life governed by compliance, mouse-clicks, and predictability. Where will it end? Less likely in a car upside down in a ditch I suppose. These will be their stories to tell.

December 5, Year One

Tried to sleep with Camille – she snored.

Over the next several months, I'll take trazodone as well as an array of calm-inducing supplements and Unisom to help me sleep.

Kids today generally lead lower-risk and often more sheltered lives than I did as a young teen, and I fear it might be stunting their development and causing unforeseeable consequences. Like limiting their ability to solve basic life tasks such as: how to set up a tent, build a fire, fix a flat, walk to school, or even drive to school. They are subjugated by overbearing, overly conscientious parents trying to do the right thing in a world that appears to be riddled with just too much risk for their own children to go it alone. Lest we forget.

With fewer opportunities to interact with the world, kids may become lost or even subverted by other, higher-risk enticements. The stakes couldn't be higher. There's more pressure than ever for kids to succeed. And I believe we've only made it more difficult for them by limiting access to experiences necessary to cultivate independence. We are hands-on creatures, and the best teachers often reside outside the confines of our own four walls. As parents, we're paranoid because we've seen too much and are hesitant to expose our children to anything that may be harmful. And consequently, many of life's magnificent opportunities to discover and learn are lost. We're a generation of hypocrites, caught in a society of our own making, in which the pendulum has swung just a little too far to one side. If she wants to jump out of a plane, let her jump out of the stupid plane. And yes, there's a chance she might get hurt.

December 10, Year One

Symptoms are more defined. Foreboding anxiety messes with my mood – a sinking feeling over-powering my sense of wellbeing. It's ever-present and ebbs and flows throughout the day. Little things agitate me. A definite distraction and, at times, burdensome.

Like me, the three knuckleheads I mostly hung out with in high school were misfits. They'd come from divorced families (I was the exception), all with moderately liberal-minded upbringings. We were, for the most part, without religious affiliation and didn't identify with any particular group. Other than the fact we happened to be White, we were without tribe. This left us with no substantive way forward as to who we were supposed to be as individuals. We were, as it were, left to our own devices to figure things out, survive, or flounder; to bide our time until it was our time to strike out on our own. And with this came a fair amount of confusion and that sense of feeling adrift – questioning authority, the way things were, our purpose and place in this world. We were all suffering quietly in our own way. This holds true for every generation of young people. Whatever "burden" we carry as adults we manage to pass along to our children: eeny, meeny, miny, moe ... As I watch my kids with their friends, it's clear that wherever we go, our mistakes and ignorance – reactions to broken relationships, insecurities, racial biases – all come along for the ride.

He had that Chanel-model look, a cross between a young Ted Danson and someone who had just lost their dog. The deep cleft chin and expressive eyebrows accentuated a certain quirkiness about him – a trait that was always fun to be around. Pat had a penchant for the finer things too evident in the way he dressed and his accouterments, and he could grow formidable facial stubble from the age of fifteen. It was these attributes we'd rely on heavily when it came to acquiring beer for the evening. Pat also loved to drive, part and parcel of a son whose father owned a Chevy dealership. So, from the age of sixteen onward, he was the go-to guy when it came to getting out and exploring our own horizons.

Pat and I had decided to do a little pre-functioning one Friday night before a high school dance. Nothing unusual, except that this time we'd managed to get our hands on a fifth of rum that his dad had set aside for an upcoming Christmas party. We cranked up some Bowie and Prince in his S-10 while I knocked back half the bottle in about thirty minutes. I was fine until shortly after we arrived, at which point Pat and I had gotten separated, and things began to fade. The next thing I knew, I was waking up in my bed, clothed and wet. A few spotty snippets from the night before started to come back – trying to stay upright on the dance floor, running through dark hallways, and hurling up a Big Mac in an evergreen bush outside the school. Somehow, I got a ride with an acquaintance and instinctively found my way home, but I could have ended up anywhere. Pat did what he could to fill in the blanks, but several hours of the previous night were just plain gone. How I didn't end up in the ER or a holding cell is beyond me.

Doug and I struck up a friendship in the seventh grade through our older brothers Scott and Shane. He was of average height, handsome with sharp features, and well-mannered. I'd had more life experience than he had up to this point (having lived on both coasts), while his worldview had mostly been limited to his immediate neighborhood. We hit it off right away and soon discovered that we shared a love for pyrotechnics. That spring, we conspired to acquire a large box of fireworks through mail-order and had it delivered to his home. His dad, a lieutenant in the fire department, wasn't too thrilled, but we managed to divvy up the cache and set to work to annoy the shit out of the neighborhood.

We spent many afternoons pretending to be soldiers in some co-lossal battle, crawling on our bellies in the tall grass adjacent to my family's home, shooting bottle rockets at each other's heads. Fortunately, neither one of us lost an eye that summer. But later that fall, he tried – screwing around with a rubber band in our living room, only to have it snap back and scratch his cornea. He could still see fine, but apparently, it was enough to keep him out of flight school. My only regret is that I wasn't there for him when he went through the passing of Shane to cancer, followed a few years later by his dad, who succumbed to a similar illness. I wish I knew then or at least was better able to express what mattered most.

If not for his 6'5" athletic frame, it would have been easier to describe Paul as having slightly feminine features: Michael Landon with a dash of Jane Russell. He had the characteristics of a Disney leading man, with big brown eyes, high cheekbones, full lips, and thick brown wavy hair. Scholastically, Paul was the smartest of the bunch and probably the most conflicted. His father, a college professor, left home when he was young, leaving his mother to raise him and his sister. Paul was inherently introverted and a bit shy and yet exhibited a heightened drive to immerse himself in whatever he happened to be pursuing at the time. Paul was highly creative and excelled at almost anything he'd set his mind to. He started playing basketball at a relatively late age (I think he was about fourteen), and by the time he had graduated high school was one of the top players in the league. Despite dropping out of Cooper Union to play guitar and work at a bookstore back in Seattle, Paul helped Doug get into Columbia graduate school by rewriting his essay. He could have chosen a career doing whatever he wanted but decided to follow his heart instead. A noble pursuit.

Meanwhile, Pat's affiliation with the dealership afforded us all kinds of opportunities. A red convertible MG Midget one week, a '68 Camaro the next. Often, the pick of the litter to accessorize the night – and when they're not your own, you can afford to be a little harder on them. We would venture off-road with non-off-road vehicles. Test the brakes and accelerator in the middle of the night in front of an unsuspecting acquaintance's house. Take laps on the school track, only to end up in an embankment stuck in the bushes. Or see how many front-end grilles we could smash on the same section of the interstate (these were unplanned). Or how many girls we could squeeze into a Corvette (five – plus the two of us). While in college, Pat got a wake-up call on a stretch of gravel when he rolled one of those cars, but luckily, he was fine. Rumor has it he didn't even spill his drink.

When Doug wasn't with a girlfriend, the four of us, or a combination thereof, would cruise Seattle proper, pick up some beer or wine coolers and maybe score a little weed in the University District, then swing by an all-ages club in pursuit of some chicks. We'd strike out mostly, which often led to a late-night Dick's run to quench the dry mouth and hunger that would have set in by then. Most weekends were a rinse and repeat – cruise, beers, music, girls, food – that's how we rolled.

We dabbled in sports, school, and extracurricular activities but longed for bigger and better things, whatever the hell that meant – not commit to too much, only do what was necessary, find ways to have fun, and not inflict too much damage in the process. But once these years passed, we began to drift apart. Paul and I would meet up on occasion, and we even lived together with a couple of other guys for about a year after college. But as family and other obligations began to take root, our encounters became less frequent.

The four of us ended up just fine, despite our mishaps. Doug became a successful international business consultant and currently lives in Vietnam with his wife and two children. Pat owns a lucrative high-end retail furniture business in Portland, Oregon, enjoying the good life. And Paul became an independent construction contractor and proprietor and still resides in Seattle.

There were others, of course, but to properly account for all of them would mean a whole other book. There was Kathy, whose silhouette wrought carnage on my young male psyche, especially the time she asked for a kiss and I panicked; her twin sister, Tonya, with who I shared a secret-secret crush – neither one of us had the courage to admit it and risk the friendship; Joelle, who I obsessed over as I wondered what it would be like if we could be together forever – and fortunately was smart enough to realize there were more important things ahead; impressionable, friendly Erik, who probably would have been better off never meeting me – we shared many coming-of-age adventures together – playing badminton, climbing trees, discovering whiskey; Dan, who had a steely wit and would step up to any challenge, like the time we wagered to see who could drink the most beer during world history class, he edged me out by a swig – who was I to bet against a four-time state wrestling finalist; Ken, whose antics won him legendary status as a legitimate crazy-man, and whose loyalty as a friend set the bar for what we all must strive to achieve in the truest sense of the word; Gregg, who rose from mediocrity to self-realization through hard work and determination in all aspects of his life – athletic, professional, and personal – he still remains the hero of my dreams; and Michelle, with who I spent nights holding hands watching TV on her couch, our innocence developing into a kindred bond that is certain to outlast our time here on earth. Without any of these encounters, acquaintances, false starts, and reckless moments, which defined and encapsulated those years, I'd be a different person.

December 26, Year One

Two months in and still experiencing symptoms. Feelings of sadness, emotional flatness, some depression. Lots of real anxieties, worries. Need to learn not to look too pessimistically at things. Relearn to be optimistic. Worries aren't real – it's NOT productive to dwell on negative outcomes that may or may not happen. Need to open my heart up to joy and think positively about life.

Some thoughts can invoke worry – it's a bottomless pit. But I must recognize this. And choose to accept rather than spend too much time peering down the well. Even a bottomless hole has a sky at the other end. I can choose to look down and ascend or look up and scale the wall.

We were all adrift to a certain degree, and maybe that's what brought us together. Most of us are at this age, but some have a higher sense of purpose than others. Those few with a clear vision for what they want out of life expressed through their commitment to their chosen craft. The artist who'd be recognized one day for elevating the Hollywood special effects industry. The star athlete who was instrumental in advancing soccer for millions of young women around the world. And the actor who went on to play Dwight in The Office, among many other notable roles. But we four seemed destined to blend in with the woodwork. Content to hang out on the periphery, observe and do our own thing. And it is its own miracle that we survived some of those "own" things. Countless nights, partying without impunity; in places that we should have never been, trolling the city, meeting like-minded kids seeking their own fun, teasing fate, discovering their essence, each of us in our own way.

December 29, Year One

Experienced a lot of anxiety last night, more than usual. This was scary. I woke numerous times, finally got out of bed, and wept. Was able to calm down after a while. Emerging out of the blue once again. Tremendous humming in the head.

One Saturday in the wee hours of the night, having exhausted our meager supply of beer, I strolled into a downtown deli on Second Avenue. It was a popular quick mart, bustling with patrons and a hot spot for the local police. I headed to the cooler towards the back of the store and loaded up as many forty-ounce, wide-mouth Mickey's I could stuff into the crook of my arm. The drinking age was twenty-one, and I was barely eighteen, motivated by the thought that if I could pull this off, I'd be the hero of the night. The two girls and guy-friend I was with were waiting in the car, counting on me to come through. I had just enough liquid courage left to fuel my confidence and, like the resetting of toppled bowling pins, carefully placed the bottles onto the counter. And with that, the teller rang me up and bagged my winnings. I then calmly made my way past the four cops positioned between me and the exit. They were too distracted to pay much attention, busying themselves with coffee, conversation, and doughnuts. Mission accomplished.

We spent the rest of the evening drinking and smoking in Erik's '71 Nova in a dark, sketchy downtown alley – blasting the tunes, partying like it was 1999. Try as I might to replicate that magical feeling experienced years earlier with Kristen in the back seat of that old Ford, it wasn't meant to be: just another futile attempt. Despite the beer buzz, the enthusiastic and willing blond and blue-eyed candidate didn't stand a chance. Some things just can't be forced. She was a wonderful person and all that, but the feeling I was chasing was just too elusive, and I had no desire to press things. I was on an island of my own making, in search of fulfillment in something (or someone) that had become progressively unattainable. Sometime after 1:00 a.m., a tap on the glass prompted us to leave. The undercover officer explained that this wasn't the safest place for us to be and urged us to head on home.

As a young person growing up in the eighties, unless it happened to you, bad things generally didn't matter because you were more often two or three steps removed from the situation. Maybe you'd hear about it on the news or later that week at school – some other group of kids who ended upside down in a ditch or wrapped around a tree. Nowadays, everybody hears about these things, in real-time, live-streamed in graphic detail. Today, there's no excuse to even mess around – why bother? Your parents won't let you anyway. In fact, if you do, you're only "inviting" trouble. Back then, right or wrong, it's what we did, many times over, on countless Friday and Saturday nights.

January 4, Year One

My goal today is to make the most of things and cope with the symptoms. Accept them as they come and try not to fight against them. As I accomplish this each day, that is a success.

FOUR

Early Jobs

I've always been drawn to doing things my way rather than con-
forming to how things should be done. For the most part, this has
worked to my advantage – finding alternative solutions rather than
following a prescribed path. But opting for this approach often
meant having to do things over, two or even three times, before
finally figuring it out or tossing in the towel altogether.

Mainstream career success was never something I aspired to
achieve. I think this mindset is due partly to my relationship with
school and academics. Learning was a challenge for me. I was an
antsy kid, especially with activities that I could care less about –
which included almost anything to do with school, except for art
classes, which were a constant outlet for me since early childhood.
To capture and retain my interest was difficult. I loathed being test-
ed and evaluated to measure my effectiveness in any facet of who I
was or could become. These deficits or disadvantages, self-inflicted
or inborn, amounted to a bit of a chip on my shoulder. A non-con-
formist mentality set in. Which translated into a stubborn desire to
work for myself and steer clear of the more traditional career path.

I believed that I'd blaze my own trail, create something unique,
figure things out along the way – that I wouldn't have to surrender
my waking hours to the agenda of another person's pursuits. Combined with my desire to work independently and inherent drive to
solve problems creatively, I felt that a self-reliant subsistence was
my destiny.

At an early age, this inner drive spawned an entrepreneurial side. Over summer breaks, I'd canvas the neighborhood with flyers, looking for work as a house painter. This proved to be lucrative, and eventually, I saved enough money to buy more tools and equipment. I excelled at being my own boss, calling the shots, and enjoyed the satisfaction of returning someone's home to its original luster. I didn't have anyone breathing down my neck, and the owners appreciated the work.

My first real job was at the local Y, making $3.80 an hour providing after-school care for kids. I wasn't thrilled about the role, but it was nice to have extra cash to fund those weekends. The job came with a lot of responsibility. At barely seventeen, with maybe a couple hundred hours of driving experience, I was tasked with picking up kids from across the school district in a sixteen-seat passenger van. And then delivering them back to the Y, where we and a couple of other (slightly more experienced) employees engaged in various games and activities until their parents collected them at the end of the workday. Nowadays, I can't imagine anyone entrusting the safety of their children to the care of a seventeen-year-old male driver. Let alone to me, a highly distractable not particularly together, high school punk. Today, Amazon drivers must be twenty-one to deliver toilet paper to your home. My, how times have changed.

One of the responsibilities I had (come to learn) was to ensure that a young boy had access to the bathroom. He was a wise-ass kid of about fourteen who had MS and needed assistance tending to his most personal needs. What athletic prowess I did have qualified me for the task, which turned out to be quite physically demanding.

It took a couple of attempts, but once we had it down, he'd prompt me with a look and smirk, and I'd know it was time: the clock was ticking. I'd quickly wheel him into the bathroom, align him next to the stall, secure the wheels, and carefully hoist him up from under his armpits with one arm and lift him out of his chair. I'd balance myself on one foot, so I could untangle his feet with the other and then awkwardly spin him over the seat. I'd maneuver his pants off with my free hand – why he wore a belt I'll never know – and lower him down as best I could. By this point, my arm would be trembling, resulting in a landing not as smooth as either of us would have preferred. And then, of course, wait for him to do his business, clean him up, and reverse the sequence. I had no one to show me how to do this. I just winged it. It was the first time I was called on to help another person in this way. To assist with an activity most of us take for granted. In hindsight, it was my privilege. This was his gift to me. Three-eighty went a long way back then.

Between house-painting gigs, I worked part-time at a local Shakey's Pizza Parlor, making crust for my brother Scott, who happened to be the store manager at the time. (Apparently, it was difficult to find competent crust makers.) It was a mindless job, and I eventually became skilled at it – knocking out dozens of "skins" over the course of a few hours. It was a risky endeavor, feeding the dough into a machine that could easily chew your fingers off if you weren't paying attention. If ever there were an opportunity to start a homegrown pandemic, it would have happened somewhere between those ripe batches of dough, the exposed pizza trays, and the not-so-pristine hands of a seventeen-year-old boy. It's a good thing those ovens were hot.

During college, I worked part-time as a lab courier for Northwest Hospital. It paid fourteen bucks an hour, which was a mint at the time, and included full health benefits. It provided just enough income to cover most of my rent and food and a couple of nights out with friends. The kid who trained me happened to have his jaw wired shut due to a spill he had taken on his bike. He slurped chocolate milk through a straw as he drove from place to place like a crazed maniac. Between the constant slurping and drooling, relentless stop and go, the exhaust fumes, and that chocolate-milky whiff, I had to have him pull over more than once just to keep from hurling. Once I got the route down, I could fly through the pick-ups and drop-offs with ease, which occasionally allowed for a window of time to do whatever the whims of a young, virile twenty-something fancied. Over about a year and a half, I survived one blown transmission, a speeding ticket, and other activities one should not consider while on the clock.

January 8, Year One

Today marked the day of most progress. I felt much better cognitively than I have in several months. Aware that I'm not 100 percent but experiencing an improvement. Healing has taken place – we'll see if this is temporary or lasting. Nevertheless, it's reassuring to feel better. The change is most welcome.

FIVE

THE COLLEGE YEARS

I thought my direction and purpose would have been clearer as I prepared to head off to college. Maybe that is how most of us feel at this point in our lives – a built-in sense of "not there yet" as an incentive to push forward and figure things out as we go. But for me, this lack of vision was unsettling. I wasn't overly excited about going, and at the same time, I felt I had no other option. So, off I went anyway – academically exposed, not particularly well prepared, with little ambition nor motivation to fuel me. Once again, I was rudderless and adrift.

I was not a particularly adept student. I had struggled with reading, focus, and attention throughout my schooling. However, I did have an advantage knowing that I was going to pursue a degree in fine arts – I mean, what the hell else was I supposed to do? Art was one of the few things that I enjoyed and knew I could do well. I applied to Washington State University and Evergreen College but didn't really like the Evergreen vibe. More importantly, WSU had an outstanding fine arts program. Which also meant that there would be a good chance that I would meet like-minded people. I was accepted to WSU, as most kids were at the time (as the joke went), and saw it as an added bonus that Scott would be wrapping up his final year there as well.

I went through Greek Rush, a process in which new recruits were paraded around frat row to see who's worthy of membership and who is not. Suffice to say, if you wanted a particular house and

they did not want you, you could just as easily find yourself relegated to a life in the dorms, dejected, along with all the other unfortunate misfits: "have a nice day." Fortunately, that was not my fate,
and I ended up (not so serendipitously) selecting the house that
Scott had joined a few years earlier.

My brother had established himself as quite the legend within
the frat ecosphere: a demigod, revered by his peers and feared by
those of lesser rank. One capable of achieving substantial feats of
alcohol consumption and overt displays of superhuman strength
demonstrated, albeit playfully, on willing yet apprehensive under-
classmen intent on taking down the giant, to no avail. And, I might
add, who also happened to have racked up an impressive roster of
sorority conquests. I had mixed feelings about all this. On the one
hand, I was following in his footsteps and hoping to measure up,
and on the other, deep down, I knew this scene wasn't for me.

I spent most of that first year acquainting myself with fraternity
life and adjusting to the rigorous class schedule. Despite the cards
that I had been dealt, I wanted to prove to myself that I could do
both well. The house rules were naturally weird, but it was up to us
newbies to scrub the toilets and keep the place relatively functional. The food was terrible. Ernie, a long-time retired Navy veteran,
came in twice a day to prep lunch and dinner – mostly Chef Boyard-
ee stuff: lots of macaroni dishes and God knows what else. I observe
my kids today as they head off to their schools with well-considered
nutritional meal plans and marvel at how far we've come.

The sleeping situation was ghastly, especially for those of us with
a sensitive disposition. We slept in a large, cavernous room equipped
with military-style bunk beds crammed end-to-end. Spanning the
back wall along the perimeter of the ceiling were a half dozen un-
dersized windows which let in minimal light and were always kept
open, regardless of the time of year. During the winter months,
it was not unusual to wake up with a coating of frost on your top
cover – it's a wonder nobody froze to death. Parties galore spilled
out onto the front lawn with music blaring, empty kegs stacked

haphazardly and often culminated with a late-night tuck-in from the campus police. Mornings met with the nauseating odor of Ernie's signature bile mixed with beer swill and bodies tucked away in odd places – victims of indelible-ink body-art adorned with shaving cream laying in repose (fig. 13, p. 189). And if you were paying attention, you might spot a weary-eyed girl wandering the halls. For the most part, I stayed out of the fray, but I did witness an unfortunate few get sucked in and spat out, having succumbed to the perils of college drinking and an unforgiving class schedule.

I enjoyed many of my classes at WSU and began to thrive. By now, I was getting to know my academic strengths and vulnerabilities, and I made a conscious effort to steer clear of the more demanding courses. (To pursue a fine arts degree meant you didn't have to take a whole lot of math). It was a women's studies professor who showed me how poor my writing skills had become. She was the first person to care enough to take the time to provide me with an honest assessment of where things stood. From that point forward, I began to pay more attention to the power of the written word and the impact it can have on others.

I also took as many astronomy classes as possible – until the math and physics got too complicated. The subject gave me a renewed appreciation for what it had taken to hurl that oversized lipstick case into the sky so many years earlier. More importantly, it provided context for how our world came to be as well as the origins of humans and life in general. For me, astronomy illuminated our true birthplace. It also opened my eyes to how fragile we really are, that "pale blue dot" floating amongst a sea of blackness, and made me consider the noble choice and responsibility we all face to maintain its harmonious ecological state. I think the foundations of astronomy should be taught earlier in school, so people understand and appreciate how good we've got it.

I excelled at art and really enjoyed figure drawing. There was something about drawing a live model that I found to be invigorating – it brought me out of my head and into what was happening in the moment. It was an activity that I found nourishing, which enabled me to express myself through line and charcoal. Plus, I got to look at naked women all day. I soon discovered that "substantial" models were far more interesting to draw than the physically toned or what might generally be considered "attractive" body types. Heavyset people have far more to offer by way of curves, volume, and shadow than those who are lean. One afternoon, an attractive young woman got assigned to one of our sessions. I found her to be less than a suitable sitter. She was pleasant to look at but distracting. For one thing, she lacked volume, which made her uninteresting to draw. When it comes to life drawing, go big or go home.

Early on, I struck up a friendship with one of the male models, Russ. He was a graduate student enrolled in the veterinary program earning decent money modeling as a sitter for the art department. Russ was a fit, good-looking, and relatable guy. He was confident and friendly, with shoulder-length blond hair and enviable abs. Russ was the kind of guy that most women couldn't help but steal a glance at, and I think he knew it – but not in a bad way. Every hour or so, he'd walk around the studio to have a look at the work. It was amusing to watch the girls blush as he looked over their shoulders and commented on his likeness, his parts dangling within inches of their personal space. In all fairness, I think they, too, were distracted. I'm sure Russ is fat and bald by now and interesting to draw.

January 14, Year One

I'm worried about the uncertainties of my cognitive state. I must reassure myself that this is part of the healing process. I'm feeling anxious about taking trazodone. I think its effects are negligible, and I'll wean off soon so I can work my way back to a natural sleep pattern.

During the latter half of that first year, I felt confident enough to venture off-campus and explore the surrounding community. I had settled into school and was gravitating towards people with shared creative interests, such as the theatre majors, musicians, and other artistic types – those "misfits" who would never have stood a chance at making it into the fraternity. Not that this particular fraternity was toxic by any means. The house was more progressive and tolerant than most, the leadership was sound, and I got along with everyone in my pledge class. My assigned roommates, "Stay-Puft," Joe, and Bill, were all friendly and cordial – we just didn't have a lot in common. It wasn't that I was better than my housemates – I became more interested in interacting with people who fell outside of the mainstream college Greek life.

I met some fun and interesting people during the final few months of that first year, at private parties and other social gatherings. Sometimes we'd hitchhike our way to Moscow Idaho, a college town located ten miles east, just on the other side of the state line, where the drinking age was nineteen. We'd hit a few alternative bars or clubs or catch a show at the nearby university – then after we'd got our fill, thumb a ride back home. The Moscow-to-Pullman highway was once infamous for being one of the deadliest stretches of road in the country – too many drunk college kids lost to their youth.

She was fun, creative, and a couple years older than me. She worked as a DJ for the campus radio station and was well-connected within the social scene. She too was an art major, and it was through these associations we met and developed a mutual and lasting friendship. We were both searching for something, and I suppose we each had a vacancy to fill, but she was more mature and self-aware than me, albeit wounded in different ways. At the time I didn't realize it, but I wasn't ready to commit. It was too soon – I was still adrift. She was looking to build a career and I felt insecure about where things were headed. She graduated and relocated to Seattle, and I transferred to the University of Washington shortly thereafter to pursue a degree in graphic design. But after a couple years of fits and starts, reality caught up with us, and we parted ways.

Despite my background in fine arts and two years' worth of academic credits, the design program at the UW essentially required me to start over, which meant my parents and I were paying for two additional years of college tuition – mostly my parents. Given the cost of school nowadays, this wouldn't even have been a consideration today. I moved back and forth between apartments and home over the next couple of years and was at home when I met my future wife in the middle of my senior year. Why she fell for a university student who still lived with his parents, I'll never know.

A lot of people I hung out with while going to school were either in a band or knew someone who was, which often meant going out to watch live music at someone's house, a bar, or a club. One of those nights a half dozen of us huddled around a friend's cramped kitchen, playing guitars, and keeping time with makeshift instruments. Among them were Pete Droge and Stone Gossard, jamming away on a rendition of "Free Bird." It was quite the spectacle: a bunch of guys immersed in the moment, the strain of the chords reflected on their faces, swapping bars. This was before the fame when a few friends and a place to hang out was enough. They had no idea what lay ahead. That one day they'd achieve their own idol status, to be pinned up on someone else's wall, a million miles removed from this moment in time.

So, here we are today, sending our kids off to college – and a familiar tale emerges. I see my eldest somewhat adrift, seeking direction and purpose. What does he need that I didn't get during this time in my life – mentorship, affirmation? Support to pursue and develop more fulfilling interests? Less pressure to commercialize his skill set, and (if I may borrow a page from Paul's playbook) more encouragement to follow his heart? I think that kind of support from an early age may very well have sent me down an entirely different path. As the years have revealed, I haven't been particularly content in the field I chose because I've felt like I've had to subscribe to a role that I wasn't quite cut out for. My optimism tells me that in the end, it will work out fine. But it will not have been without its challenges and a lot of years spent wondering what could have been.

My parents loved me unconditionally, but did they support me when I needed it most? Who knows. They did what they thought was best. What our kids want may not fit our vision for them, but what sparks their passion means everything. I'm not speaking of material provisions, but the emotional support we all need to flourish. To let go and nourish their being is to give them permission to pursue a path of their own making. This is the lesson that we parents must learn.

January 27, Year One

Experienced a fair amount of cognitive confusion and brain fog throughout the day. Headache still. Need to remind myself constantly of the evolution of change that is happening, albeit slowly. One day closer. This will pass. Tired of explaining the symptoms to people. Can't blame them for tuning out.

The Road Trip

Ten years would pass before I would see her again. The letters and phone calls had long since stopped. But the persistence of her memory had been fully seared into my gut. It was the summer of '87, and I was determined to see it through. I was entering my fourth year at the University of Washington and was getting a bit antsy. A road trip was what I needed. This time, and for the first time, it would be a journey on my own terms, not tethered to some family agenda, stopover, or photo-op (fig. 14, p. 189). This trip had a single purpose – to once and for all face what had now become deeply seeded – the past. And her place in it.

I had never driven the highways outside of Chicago before. But, on this last day of my two-day marathon drive, without GPS and with only a tattered map in hand, something about those roads began to look familiar. As I passed through the tollways and vestiges of the roads' history, the McDonald's straddling the freeway, the way the trees encroached on the interstate and filled in the horizon, I could sense I was getting close. Something in the ether had guided me this far – take this exit, make this right, just a little further – and within a short while, I found myself directly in front of her house, curbside – no backtracking, just sitting there, idling.

And there I sat, nervous with anticipation, peering through the passenger window, my exhausted companion puffing out blue rings. The brick Tudor just as I remembered: brown trim, arched facade, weathered oak door. The door behind which a decade earlier we had tittered over hot cocoa, thawing out from afternoons of ice skating, talking about why that picture hung on the kitchen wall. I called and left a message a few days earlier to provide her with plenty of opportunity to escape. I wondered whether she'd even be there.

Heart pounding, I gathered the courage to leave the sanctuary of my protective dome and began the short trek up the walkway. And with each step, I felt the years that divided us closing in. As I approached, I could see the shadows of the leaves dancing across the yard and sensed the thick summer air gripping my body. The bugs scattered in flight, creating the illusion of sparks flittering about, as if the sky were nervous and knew something was afoot. The smells and sounds of home all came rushing back as if I'd never left.

As I lifted the knocker, I felt the accumulation of years pooling up in the back of my throat. Only a moment and a sliver of space remained between it and the strike plate, soon to connect the long-awaited gap. Two lives once again brought together by this single act – is there such a thing as destiny? I had accepted that this would mean more to me than her, but what if she felt the same way? After two light taps and a few breaths, I heard the soft footfall of a person approaching, then the sound of the latch, followed by the hiss of the door as it glided gently across the hardwoods – and there she stood, looking back, but this time it wasn't a dream.

I was immediately caught by her generous smile and welcoming eyes. Then suddenly, everything became real. It was her, but something was different. She had changed. I had changed. By now, even she couldn't have matched the image that I had formed of her in my mind. It was then that I realized I didn't know her. We had both become different people, and the vision I had built up over the years had simply become that: a fantasy. Those nights as a young boy crying myself to sleep, the many months and years dreaming of what it would be like to be together again, the memories of our time in that old Ford – certainly she must have felt the same way – all reconciled in an instant.

We talked for an hour about what we'd been doing over the years. And I dropped a few clues about the impact she had on my life. But I knew it was a narrative of my own making, built upon insecurities curated over time. The world isn't always as it seems. And how we perceive it, memories, of love, in particular, can be a distraction if left to fester. A diversion from the many real and meaningful things happening all around us at any given moment. We hugged and said goodbye. I was free.

January 31, Year One

One step away from no trazodone. Slept OK. Looks like I'm sleeping equal to or better than I was before going off alprazolam. That's progress! There is the sensation of pressure in the head and the narrowing of mental faculties, which can be somewhat claustrophobic – like walls closing in. Focus and clarity become difficult. My thinking is a step behind. Fear emerges about how much longer this will continue – but I try not to spend too much time dwelling on those thoughts – rather, accept what is happening at each moment as the way it is.

SEVEN··········

STEPHEN

The dimly lit room in the dead of night had an eeriness about it as if it were trying to tell me something. The landscape my mom had painted decades earlier, hanging at the foot of the bed, began to vibrate and move from within as if the shapes were melding and contorting (fig. 15, p. 189). The room itself had become blurry, without borders or edges. The corners lacked definition as if I could simply walk off into the shadows or something could enter from the outside. I felt exposed and vulnerable. I sat up and was wide awake, and yet the unearthly qualities persisted. There was this palpable energy all around me, an aura that was real and wanting. Then, after an hour or so, it dissipated.

It was late summer of '89, and I had been staying with my parents on Capitol Hill for a few months, sleeping in the guest bedroom at the back of the house. I was about midway through school, and nothing out of the ordinary was happening in my life. Things were calm for a change. It was just another Tuesday as I headed off to bed sometime before midnight in preparation for another day of classes.

But this night, I was awakened by this strange energy. Not in reaction to any dream or terrible thought, it seemed to emanate from within the room. I was then overcome by an uneasy feeling – like something was attempting to tap into my inner self and grab my attention as if a kind of mental-osmosis was taking place. It was even more strange this went on for two consecutive nights, at which point, more out of curiosity than anything, I welcomed the presence more openly. I then felt a certain intensity take hold – a sensation even more visceral than the night before. And then a profound sense of sorrow came over me. I felt compelled to acknowledge its existence and invite whatever it was to move on, "I'm aware of you, it's OK … but it's time to go". And that was it. The strange apparition was gone.

A few days later, she called. We thought it was just an unfortunate misdial. The message left on my parents' answering machine was incoherent and garbled. The best we could discern was that it was a distraught woman, sobbing on the other end, out of context from anything that was happening in our lives at the time – removed from the people we knew, its meaning lost. I thought nothing more of it.

In the spring of '88, I had finally reconnected by phone with my childhood best friend, Stephen (fig. 16, p. 189). Our parents had shared interests that brought us together before we could walk. Our mothers were artists, and our fathers had worked together as photojournalists. We reveled in our playdates and shared a penchant for getting into trouble. We played hide-and-go-seek together, enjoyed countless sleepovers, and spent many summer nights playing kick-the-can. I distinctly remember hitting him in the head with a wooden block. I couldn't have been more than two, still in diapers; it is one of my earliest memories. I'll never forget that trickle of blood as it ran down his cheek, and then my mom swooped me away. We reminisced for about an hour and discussed plans to one day ride our bikes across the country together.

Our families participated in King Richard's Renaissance Faire for several weekends over a few glorious summers. We'd run barefoot through the woods, exploring the many artisan booths, venues, and games. We feasted on roasted corn and spent hours observing the belly dancers as they rolled coins across their stomachs and then watched battle reenactments in the open spaces adjacent to the stage. We scaled structures at dusk, scoured the archery range for lost arrows, and dodged countless flaming marshmallows by the campfire. We toughened our hands and feet climbing trees and playing in the nearby fields. Setting up, knocking down, and jumping off bales of hay until we were exhausted and ready to do it all over again the next day (fig. 17, p. 190).

We had shared the time of our lives together, storylines we'd recount time and time again over the years: reciting them in school essays, reliving them in our thoughts and dreams. We had this in common – a shared coming of age, a union forged since early childhood. And I looked forward to one day reconnecting with the only person who understood this and what it all meant. And I know he did too. But not like this.

Stephen had shot himself in the head. He lay in a hospital bed, in a coma, plugged into life support. He was all but barely there, kept alive by a breathing tube, a few wires, and maybe one last piece of unfinished business. Stephen was living in Colorado at the time – attending the Olympic Academy while training as a track cyclist, and a family quarrel and life's circumstances had conspired to bring him to this current state. Those two nights I lay awake in my parent's guestroom, beckoning the intruder to depart, coincided with his final moments when I said it was OK to move on. And maybe that's all he needed. The young woman who left a message on the machine was his sister. Too many years had passed, and she was so upset. It took a few days for their dad to get a hold of us and sort things out, but I already knew something had happened. Stephen was gone.

Those who take their own life may very well feel a profound sense of regret. And in their final moments, make a last-ditch effort to reconnect with those most meaningful to them. A communion reserved for relationships in which time and distance melt away, and the transcendental and physical worlds know little boundary. My gift to him was forgiveness, or maybe to heed his invitation to share in his final moments – that sinking feeling, the emptiness – was his gift to me. His way of saying, "it's up to you to see this through; and although we shared those precious times, the adventure continues. There remains much life to live. Take that ride."

Honestly, I think it was as much a coincidental encounter as a deliberate act of goodwill on my part. I could have just as easily ignored the "invitation" and shut it out. Sometimes we find ourselves at the hand of someone in need. An opportunity to make a difference in the right moment, as in this instance when our souls briefly crossed paths. He reached out, and I paid attention. I acknowledged his pain, and we reconnected on some level, in effect granting him permission to move on – or say goodbye, or share in one last adventure, to kick the can and free the jail. He passed at that moment – I felt him go, and I even felt a sense of resolution when he did.

February 1, Year One

I find it difficult to explain to someone something that they've never experienced. The more I try to talk about it, the crazier it sounds because from the outside I look fine, but on the inside, I'm like, "who the hell am I?" I describe it as a place, deep down, at the emotional core, that assures that things are OK, as now having been compromised. My emotional barometer is broken, leaving me feeling vulnerable. My home base is no longer on stable ground. It's unsettling. Having practiced mindfulness for several months I'm able to observe that there's something inside that's constantly on high alert, knocked askew, not right from within. I observe myself in this state rather than try to affect it one way or another. To associate it with something, an experience, rather than simply allow it to be what it is – a symptom – would be to make it my own. It's not my own. It's a malfunction in the brain because of an event that happened months ago. An outcome that is temporary and yet has taken up residence in the form of whacked circuitry. It will pass eventually, I am told. Faith is to reassure myself of this truth, despite in the moment it being real and constant. Why wouldn't my doctor be held accountable? I didn't ask for this, I didn't sign a waiver.

Recently and often, I've felt subtle vibrations in my legs. Like an electric current running up and down my center. I can feel it working its way up from the bottom, shimmering up my veins, tickling the bones. There's this ever-present anxiety that's taken root, hanging out on the peripheral, nervously whittling away. A sense of constant agitation, an unsettling feeling, yet it seems to originate not from a thought or feeling, rather it's built in. This is not like any other experience I've had before – it presented abruptly and is now chronic. Even in my heightened state of mindfulness, I can sense the unwelcome sensations rattling around in my body.

EIGHT

SHE'S THE ONE

It was a Friday night, and I was enjoying the comfort of my parent's couch watching a rerun of Gilligan's Island. That's when a friend called and asked if I wanted to go to a Christmas party. I was hesitant at first. It was damp, cold, and dark outside, and the thought of leaving my cozy blanket sounded like far too much effort. But she talked me into it. I rallied, slipped on my shoes, and met up a short while later.

When we arrived, we were greeted with warm decor, candlelight, and a tasteful selection of holiday classics. There was a smattering of people, most of whom I knew, casually talking and milling around. Aside from the festive backdrop, it had the makings of a routine night out with friends. It wasn't long until I found my way back to the comfort of a couch. The perfect vantage point from which to sit and observe the rest of the evening, content to watch from afar and not get too immersed in conversation. My mood remained subdued, and I was only half-present, distracted by the lure of kicking back as things unfolded around me. My friend and I sipped on our drinks and got caught up with the events of the day. It was to be a relaxing night, something to do – although Gilligan would have sufficed fine.

The cocktails soon began to have their way, and I was finally able to summon the energy that I'd been lacking much of the evening. After about an hour, my friend Suzanne arrived with someone I'd never seen before. As they entered the room, Suzanne's companion, by her mere presence, immediately set the room ablaze with this crazy energy. The sequins from her orange dress cast speckles of light in every direction, like a shower of sparks spewing from the end of a welder's torch. It was an impossible entrance. And I was immediately overtaken by an enormous sense of awareness. I was now fully present, wide awake, and intrigued.

Suzanne was in many respects the social epicenter of the Seattle scene, so it made sense that she would know someone capable of conjuring up so much energy. Earlier in the evening, the two of them had been out doing their own thing when Suzanne suggested to her friend, who was relatively new to the area, that the Christmas party would be a great way for her to meet new people.

I immediately found this mysterious guest to be alluring and attractive. And yet it's not generally in my nature to initiate conversation, especially with someone who I felt was way out of my league. But there was something about her that made it easy. And I'd soon learn that she had taken notice of me right away as well – the quiet, curious guy kicking back on the couch. Go figure. After a quick introduction, we were hitting it off, learning more about each other, where we were from, what music we liked, covering all the bases, and then some.

We talked incessantly, well into the early hours, drinking and smoking, away from everyone else, sitting on the kitchen floor of all places. We had a lot in common. We both enjoyed art and music and connected on the little things. We shared our family stories, talked of travel – it was pleasantly weird actually, we just fit. She was very loquacious, and I was more reserved, and our personalities immediately gelled.

As the night progressed things got hazy, but we did manage to find our way back to that couch. We cuddled and kissed and drifted in and out of sleep. As the sun rose and our heads cleared, I suggested we go back to my parents' house for a cup of tea. The invitation made her a little uncomfortable initially (come to learn that "tea" can be code for something entirely different), but my intentions were genuine. I just wasn't ready for our time together to end, nor apparently was she. We revitalized our senses with some chamomile, continued to talk for a couple more hours, then exchanged phone numbers. At which point we departed, and I watched her drive off, wondering if I'd ever see her again.

She spent Christmas at her parent's home in South Dakota, where, after a little sleuthing, I was able to track her down (having *her* number didn't mean I had *their* number). We had several conversations over the phone, me fiddling with the cord once again as I lay back in bed, wondering what the future had in store. Upon her return, it didn't take long for us to realize that our lives were about to head in an entirely different direction. I knew that this was the person I wanted to be with, and she was having similar thoughts. With Camille, it wasn't an old Ford sedan that codified the relationship; she brought her own set of wheels – a red 1969 Oldsmobile Cutlass Supreme, with white leather interior, power windows, and a stock 5.7-liter V8. Fully equipped with sparks and tingles.

NINE

FORESHADOWING

The previous manager left just two weeks after Amy and I started working at the agency, so it was up to us to take charge of the influx of projects already flowing through. The work was interesting: developing branded solutions for corporations, sports franchises, and the burgeoning tech industry. Juggling multiple projects and figuring things out as we went along, setting up processes, and cranking out designs as fast as requests came in.

When Brent came on board just a few weeks later as a contractor, the three of us immediately got along. It was an instant kinship really – cajoling Amy to recount her salacious high-school escapades, sharing stories, marginally driving each other nuts. Making light in an otherwise fast-paced, deadline-driven environment. We'd tease the sales staff relentlessly as they went about their day – hurling insults over the cubicles while they were engaging clients on the phone. We had the upper hand because they relied on us to help them with new business pitches. It was all in good fun. Within a few weeks, Brent and I bonded and realized that the upcoming holiday would provide the ideal backdrop to formalize the friendship – It was go-time for bro-time.

February 4, Year One

Today caught me off guard. It was very stressful, with mounting anxiety, bringing me right back to the onset of this whole debacle. The recent lack of sleep has stoked the intensity.

Had a good cry with Camille. She asked if I wanted to see a psychologist. Reminded her that much of what I'm feeling is attributable to the cessation of alprazolam.

It was to be a Fourth of July barely to remember, yet I recall parts of it so clearly. It was a beautiful warm day at my parent's lagoon-front home in Snohomish, where they were living at the time. They were out of town for a few days, and we had the place to ourselves. We got an early start, lighting fireworks off the dock, grilling meat, drinking beer: serious dude stuff. Camille and I had not been married even a year, and of course, Brent and I had known each other for only a few months, so what better occasion to size up one another and christen the friendship.

We were both beer-drinking athletes, capable of consuming enormous amounts of brewage given the proper incentive. And the Fourth was the perfect opportunity to showcase our talents. He, an avid rugby player, thoroughly groomed from a decade of mandatory postgame celebrations and I accustomed to Thursday-thru-Saturday night outings with Camille and friends at various music venues and bars. Our shared interests were graphic design, having fun, and pleasant company over beer. We were kindred spirits and certainly would have been kick-the-can cohorts back in the day. There was something simple and comforting about the whole connection, and the feeling was mutual.

As the day progressed, Camille, Brent, and I hung out on the patio, volleying one-ups back and forth, building off the moments – knit one purl two. The ample selection of beers mixed with Zep-

pelin, Ray Vaughan, and Hendrix set the tempo for the perfect afternoon. The day soon gave way to pleasant hues of oranges, pinks,
and purples as the sky receded into evening and then into night – at
which point any remaining perception of time had simply drifted
off to sleep.

It was one of those days that you wished would never end. And
yet, in the back of your mind, knew the train would eventually
come, and it would be time to disembark. And, as 2:00, 3:00, then
4:00 a.m. came and went, we were soon confronted with the not-so
sober realization that our stop had finally arrived, and the Monday
morning staff meeting was nearly upon us.

7:00 a.m. came swiftly and without mercy. Having been on the
job for only a few months, we knew two-thirds of the department
not showing up for the all-hands-on-deck meeting would not make
for a productive beginning to the workweek, nor bode well for my
future with the company. For Brent, it was not that big of a deal. He
could afford to miss a day here and there because he wasn't a full-
time employee. Plus, if I had a choice, I would have called this one
in. I figured at least one of us earned the right to tap out.

The route to work that morning spanned about twenty miles,
the majority of which I'd never traveled before. I was in unfamiliar territory. The drive would prove challenging. Before the days
of Google-assisted navigation, and given my state of inebriation, it
seemed highly unlikely I'd make it there on time, if at all. Stuck in
some dead-end cul-de-sac or strange neighborhood, feigning car
trouble as an excuse for not making it in. Yet somehow, miraculous-
ly, I arrived without incident and with a minute to spare.

I vaguely recall entering the small, dimly lit conference room at
the front end of a group of stragglers. Space was tight, and standing
room was limited. The company was growing fast and getting relegated to the hallway meant you were less than committed to the
corporate mission. The unfortunate latecomers were subjugated to
a verbal outing and a five-dollar fine for the social fund, and I was in
no shape to handle this level of public shaming. I must have reeked

of distillates as I slithered my way through the tight quarters, and yet at the same time, I felt giddy that I'd somehow made it this far. I almost broke character and let out a laugh but managed to bite my cheek and hold it together. A tinge of panic ensued as I shuffled past my cohorts, hoping not to stumble, breathe on anyone, or get found out.

Somehow, I made it through the meeting undetected and found my way back to my desk. Amy, Brent, and I worked virtually side-by-side. Brent on my right, Amy on the left. There couldn't have been more than a couple feet between us, with no divider. And the vapors emanating from my pores must have crossed into her space. By some miracle, Brent did make his way in about an hour after me, awakened by the firm slap of Camille's hand to his rear – she wasn't going to let him off that easy. This was to be our secret. And as any two seasoned athletes can attest, shared only by those who dare compete at the highest level.

The morning crawled onward. I concentrated all my will to tap down the nausea, which was only marginally bearable. I was operating on an empty stomach and lunchtime was quickly approaching. But the thought of any kind of sustenance entering my system would have meant certain humiliation. After a few hours, my headache began to carve its way along the perimeter of my skull, from the inside-out, from the upside-down. I remained upright, barely, driven by an inner voice that kept telling me I could do this, that I would survive, that I'd stay alive. (Yes, those lyrics did pop into my head.) At one point I managed to slip away into the darkroom for about twenty minutes in an to attempt to regain some use of my senses. I can still see the second hand laboring its way past the hash marks on the clock just above the door, slamming its way forward one arduous stroke at a time: tick ... tick ... tick. It wasn't nearly enough. I was still pretty much tanked and not sure how much longer I could hang on.

After I returned to my desk, I managed to get a few things done. As I discovered, to my surprise, my focus narrows when under extreme mental duress – not so much in cerebral acuity, but rather in sheer drive, a mustering of the will to keep the gears in motion. It's like instinct kicks in, a survival mechanism intended to keep the body moving forward as if I was assaulting my own proverbial Normandy front. Midway through the day, I felt compelled to give up the charade. I looked over at Amy and with a tinge of satisfaction said, "Do you know how shit-faced I am right now?" She blurted out a laugh, as she often would when reacting to something ridiculous, commonplace given our locale. "You'd never know" she replied with a snicker. Back to work we went, and that was that.

February 5, Year One

Woke at about 12:30 a.m. Experiencing excitability and hot sweats once again. Practiced mindfulness earlier and observed the sensation of electricity traveling through my limbs – a gentle wave, like a nine-volt battery emanating from my toes.

The three of us had formed a sibling-like bond in relatively short order. But given my actions that morning, I felt my behavior must have crossed a line, invoking retribution of one kind or another, if not from Amy, then from someone else in the office. But nobody knew, nobody cared. I was just an idiot. And that, the real lesson for me in all this, was lost in the moment.

In hindsight, the big takeaway for me that day was the realization that I had a high capacity to persevere through extreme discomfort: a conjuring of the will from the deepest depths to propel myself into the next moment. It's not behavior I'd condone or recommend, but it is, nevertheless, a successful outcome despite overwhelming odds of failure. I felt physically terrible, my system awash in a mashup of lights and darks. I was on the brink of historic personal and professional disgrace. And yet, somehow, I managed to power through, proving that I could walk the line between near-incoherence and blending in with my surroundings – tasked to perform and finish out the day. To me, it was pure torture. To those around me – aside from Brent, who was no doubt clinging to life with equal desperation – it was just another day in the office. I'm glad I'll never have to go through that again.

I've run marathons in the freezing rain (fig. 18, p. 190) and experienced sickness and heartbreak, but the discomfort I subjected myself to that day proved to be the experience I'd reflect on most to keep me grounded throughout the many dark days that lay ahead. It's pathetic but true. That crazy post-Fourth-of-July bro-date day at the office, ironically, would be the catalyst I needed to help me stay connected with family, friends, and work during the most disconnected period of my life.

The experience also showed me that whatever is happening on the inside, no matter how uncomfortable or unstable, need not necessarily be reflected outwardly – at least to the extent to which you are willing to put yourself out there knowing that a no-show means getting canned. We can cave to adversity or give our best to adapt and keep going. Because the reality is, the neighbor to your left has no clue as to how you actually feel.

How I would apply this knowledge years later was beyond my comprehension at the time. And yet, "You can do this, you can survive this" would be the mantra I'd rely on for strength and motivation each morning for months – my senses so askew – having to endure a complete psychotic dick-punch. That this moronic experience would provide the lattice I needed to see me through my most challenging crisis was both absurd and, at the same time, a godsend. Everyone has a reservoir from which to draw strength, and mine just happened to originate from a massive hangover.

February 9, Year One

So much to be grateful for – the kids, Camille, reclaiming my health. I have a great family that loves me – life is good. Much to celebrate every week. This storm will pass, and the sun will shine again soon.

February 10, Year One

This was a bad day. Depressive feelings and cognitive fog closing in. Hissing in the head. Still fearful that this may be with me for some time. Need to work on positive thinking and limiting undue stress at work whenever possible. This week represents a step backward in progress.

I've been intrigued with the stars ever since I visited the Kennedy Space Center as a kid. The correlation between who we are, where we live, and those remnants of the past glittering overhead. And, to a greater extent, the notion that the more we observe and learn, the more apparent this interconnectedness becomes. Thanks to science, we know the universe is comprised of certain elements – we are all made from the same "stuff," as the late Carl Sagan would say. And yet, the more we reveal about our material existence the wider the chasm in our understanding of why any of this is happening at all.

As we look outward, we can only imagine what lies just on the other side of what we can actually see. This is true even with the best infra-red telescopes peering into the deepest recesses of space. Even as technology enables us to press our faces more firmly against the glass, we still have no idea what lurks just outside the tank. No matter how hard we try, there will always remain a beyond. And I think this applies in our daily lives as well. The further we look, the more we wonder and the further we wander. Many of us venture so far outside ourselves looking for answers, we tend to under serve the true origin of our own being – ourselves. We're simply looking in the wrong places when it comes to seeking meaningful answers to life's simple questions. Preoccupied with the notion that fulfillment must be drawn from some external source if it's not readily available from within. As a species, I think we tend to over-complicate things.

February 13, Year One

Reluctant yet desperate for answers, I was referred to a neuropsychiatrist to address the symptoms plaguing me these past several months. I'm optimistic that relief is on its way and grateful to finally have affirmation from an outside expert that what I'm experiencing is indeed real.

February 15, Year One

In addition to the EEG contraption strapped to my head, I found the in-depth dive into my entire psychological profile unnerving and taxing, given my fragile state. It seems like overkill. My hope is that through this process, Dr. Penep can help develop a healing plan. But part of me wonders why he's tossing salt into the wound.

February 17, Year One

It's been a few hours since taking Carbatrol 100 mg as prescribed by Dr. Penep. If anything, I'm feeling spacier than ever, confused, and my vision is blurrier. Will keep an eye on this. Don't know if I want to continue taking this stuff, especially if I'm intending to work. It just doesn't feel right.

I do not think the spoils of life are exclusive to the smart, the literate, or those dedicated to solving one particular theory. Achievements can only go so far. The true measure of accomplishment, I believe, is held to an entirely different standard – one of kindness. Altruistic kindness expressed through the generosity of the heart. And the "why" because it matters. We have the gift of consciousness, a capacity for empathy, and the opportunity to value one another, and a choice to embrace this heritage or not. We will be fine once we figure out kindness as a species. You can be kind in winning and be kind to your neighbor, but you cannot be kind when taking advantage of the guy next to you to get ahead. And kindness and killing generally do not go hand-in-hand. I'm not sure why it is so difficult for us humans to figure this out. We are born with this understanding, then we lose it, and if we are fortunate, spend the remainder of our days trying to reel it back in.

I cannot help but wonder why we stay in the fight – why we choose to get up in the morning when it seems that everything around is closing in, beckoning us to abandon the effort. Then I think of the stars and their role in the universe. And what they gave up paving the way for our existence. And what that process reveals to us now. I think about the crushing weight of gravity as the stars formed, grew, expanded, then eventually, after living out their purpose, imploded to a catastrophic end to forge a new beginning for others to follow. Undergoing unimaginable pressure and heat, forming heavier and more sophisticated elements. And then sending those out to seed the universe with life, as if a gift, to eventually form the "stuff" that makes up our conscious minds. I think we must also face the forces that life presents us. And not unlike the fate of stars that came before, this turbulent cycle leads to something profound within our own selves. Something important, necessary, and of a higher purpose. Kindness is a heavy element. And it too fortifies our purpose as we confront what life has to offer – the good and the bad.

There is a simple math concept I like to roll over in my head. (Not that I can solve the actual equation, it is just something I like to visualize.) The chances that any two of us should meet are infinitesimally small. The odds that you and I should have a conversation about anything are, therefore, virtually nil – such that it should not even register on any kind of galactic scale, not even a blip: as close to zilch as you can get. Therefore, me writing this sentence, let alone you are reading it, is imperceptibly less probable than you or me winning the lottery every day for the rest of our lives.

And yet, here we are. Not just you and I, but billions of unique souls. An assembly of people going about our days, passing, and bumping into one another, forming relationships with a few, scratching our own winning ticket with each and every second we breathe. Meanwhile, discrediting the vast majority of everyone else as "them," "different," "the enemy," or "inferior." But the fact remains. Mathematically speaking, none of this should be happening at all – let alone you and me and the whole world living out these profound conscious moments. Sharing in all things amazing and horrific, and real, with the capacity to contemplate and reflect upon our own unique experiences at any given moment.

We are the reflective pool of our origin, with the ability to reason and probe into the source of our own existence. Realization of the moment is our gift – and how we use it matters. Each one of us has a purpose. There is really no mystery to it, only diversions – otherwise, none of this would be happening at all. Our purpose is to live out our lives fully, with kindness, so that we may all benefit and be stronger for it. And that's good enough for me.

February 27, Year One

I met with him for the first time in his windowless, claustrophobic office. Cheap furniture, poorly lit, with pasty off-white walls – there was nothing comfortable about it. His presentation was like that of a used-car salesman. He was trying to sell me on the idea of needing his services rather than addressing the situation that was of concern to me. He wanted to attribute what I was experiencing to some latent memory, not listening to why I was seeking his help, let alone validating the series of events that I had just laid out. This was not the place for me. But got to turn over all the stones.

ENTERING THE WORKFORCE

Precariously transporting ladders on my shoulders, two-stepping my way around flower beds and other hazards. The rungs burrowing into my feet, arches aching, exposed to the elements. The distinct smell and texture of the dust. My callused and sore hands, the effect of the fumes on my senses. A full day's labor is gratifying, pushing through the pain and then getting paid for it satisfying.

Upon graduating college, I started a legitimate house-painting and light construction business. I hired a couple of friends, increased my marketing efforts, and generated steady work. I interacted well with the homeowners, and my family was impressed that I had created a marginally sustainable small business for myself. And frankly, so was I.

However, after a few years, I was no longer content with what I was doing and felt the need to pursue something different, driven by a nagging sense that I was better than the work. So, I eventually swapped out the brush for a computer and began to put my hard-earned college degree to work.

Within a short while, I got a job as an entry-level graphic designer at a marketing agency in Redmond, where I'd soon meet Brent and Amy (as well as develop that capacity to cope through high levels of distress). And although it didn't pay much, the opportunity was a way into my chosen field of study: a chance to apply what I had learned within a real-world setting. I viewed this first role as a stepping-stone towards something better and potentially even more fulfilling. Meanwhile, bide my time, keep my head down, stay the course, and work hard. And yet, I never fully understood what that elusive "better" meant, let alone what I was chasing (or evading) in the process.

The agency experience was my first opportunity to work within a creative field in a professional setting. The role exposed me to a variety of projects, and I met some fun and interesting people along the way – a whole cast of characters, including the business owners who would end up marrying their subordinates and wrecking marriages in the process. They became titans of the industry, astute business entrepreneurs known for throwing legendary parties.

After about a year and a half designing logos and t-shirts, and numerous other trinkets, I had the itch to get out on my own once again. I felt that it was time to move on and take what I'd learned to the next level. And that's when Brent and I conspired to set up our own design firm.

To keep expenses low, we began working evenings out of the garage of the home that Camille and I were renting at the time. A cozy 960-square-foot house located in the Wedgwood neighborhood ten minutes north of downtown Seattle. The home that we'd eventually end up purchasing a few years later and live in, to this day.

Our first job was for a local software start-up company designing screen interfaces for a virtual photography game. This initial project, and a fifteen-thousand-dollar loan from my father-in-law, enabled us to open our doors, and DesignSight was officially in business. We retained our previous agency as a client until I unwittingly referred to our contact as a "yak" in an email, to which she promptly responded by telling me to go do something to myself. Over the ensuing months, we grew from meager means to slightly better-than-meager means, and off we went.

After about a year, we relocated to an 'official' office straddling Lake Union on the lower eastern slope of Queen Anne. The building set on piers would sway in heavy winds, which could be disorienting. When the earthquake of '98 struck, Brent was literally caught with his pants down in the bathroom stall, soaking his shoes and pant legs as the water sloshed over the rim. It was typical for Brent to find himself in these absurd predicaments (stories for another day).

Within a year, we outgrew the office on stilts and moved into a larger place in the heart (or "bowels") of the Belltown neighborhood. We got a fabulous deal on a 2,300-square-foot space located on the second floor of an indiscreet two-story building adjacent to a local software mogul. Aside from shooing the local prostitutes out from under the stairwell on occasion, the location was perfect! It was just far enough removed from the hustle and bustle of the downtown core that you didn't feel overshadowed by the density of the tall buildings or boxed in by the noise and chaos of the city streets. We had a conference room, a reception area, several desks, seven employees to fill the seats, and a terrific view of Elliott Bay. Each workstation was equipped with the latest space-age, compact teal Apple computer, and all the gear and supplies needed to support the operation. It was a magical time – adding clients, throwing parties, and fostering relationships with the local vendors.

March 2, Year One

Slept w/Camille!!

March 3, Year One

What makes these days most difficult is the collection of symptoms that creep into my mind and body all at once. Blatant fatigue. A sense of uneasiness, a lack of focus, and a dampening of the senses. Also, a steady vibration of anxiety that is not related to any thought or worry. Ungrounded, free-flowing anxiety adding to the unsteadiness of my being. In the deeper moments of my meditation, these symptoms reveal themselves as being even more distinct – a grip on the right side of the face – an echo of adrenaline. These are the symptoms of my withdrawal – a physical response to a chemical change in my brain. Healing is slow and it has evolved and changed only slightly. Must be patient, stay the course and good days will come.

"Vater! Vater! Vater!" the taller of the two would demand as they entered the reception area unannounced. They introduced themselves as Igor and Vladimir, and we could immediately tell they were a long way from home. Igor was athletic in stature and the more talkative of the two. Later we'd learn he was an ex-Olympic Russian boxer, a few years out of his prime yet still quite capable. Strong and confident, he was fearless and charismatic. We welcomed them with cups of "Vater," which they were profusely appreciative. We chatted for a few minutes and invited them to an open house we planned to host the following evening. We made it a point every year to have a get-together. Inviting clients, prospects, family, and friends. This was a winning strategy because it was an opportunity to thank our clients (which often led to more work), and it was also the perfect excuse to throw a party without fear of retribution the next morning.

Mom had joined the agency part-time to help with marketing. She had previously worked at another agency and therefore was aware of the processes we needed to generate new business. She also shared our affinity for having a good time and was an expert in organizing social events, plus ... well ... she was my mom, and having her around was, in itself, a gift. And this year, for our open house, we had planned to double up the festivities to include my dad's retirement celebration (fig. 19, p. 190).

In addition to our client contacts and business associates, guests included my dad's colleagues and friends, photographers, managers, staffers, and, of course, the two Russian sailors we had befriended a day before the scheduled event. We gathered several of my dad's more memorable photographs and had them enlarged and hung on the wall. The large black-and-white images provided the perfect backdrop for the evening. And were a focal point for him and his friends to reminisce.

Well into the night, music blaring and Brent's mom dancing on the table, a few of us headed down to the wharf with Igor and Vladimir. Their vessel was docked about a half mile away at Elliott Bay Marina. We came bearing chocolate truffles and bottles of red wine. These gifts and the captain's discretion were our tickets to entry. Russia was under extreme economic duress at the time, and we surmised that the sailors must have been starving for something other than their standard rations of borscht, bread, and vodka. And we just happened to have what they needed to help lift their spirits.

The large ship was over a football field in length and docked parallel to the pier – and weathered by a few too many excursions at sea. We were welcomed with a warm reception as we stepped aboard, our port of entry stamped with a nod of approval. It felt surreal at first and a bit sketchy. By the act of walking up the ramp and onto the ship's deck, we were no longer home. We were aboard the Russian state, bound by maritime rules, and now part of a community of hard-core sea-worn sailors begrudgingly awaiting resupply and fuel. Having spent months at sea, these men were weary, homesick, and starved for companionship. Apart from a few higher-ranking officers, like Igor and Vladimir, the crew was confined to the vessel. The shore and all it had to offer, inaccessible to most. The view from the deck, a taunting peek at a way of life they could only dream. They were most certainly to leave with a greater sense of condemnation than they had when they arrived.

These sailors had left their families behind to fend for themselves, to endure poverty and political instability on their own. And yet, because of this unlikely encounter, two thirsty travelers, and an open-door policy, we shared a joyous encounter in the most unlikely of circumstances, disarming stereotypes and fears in the process. Affirmation that goodness from strangers knows no limits. And, despite our differing backgrounds, we shared common themes and friendship – a reminder that we are indeed all connected, if only in life's simple gestures.

March 9, Year One

Dr. Penep clearly doesn't understand the lingering effects that a rapid cessation can have, nor is he empathetic towards what I am experiencing, which is counter-productive to my healing. Despite his multiple doctorates in Neuropsychiatry, he does not have a protocol to treat what I just went through. The 100-percent fact is that most of the discomfort I'm currently experiencing is related to the cessation of alprazolam. And there's plenty of information available to suggest that these experiences are associated with stopping the medication abruptly.

Counterintuitive to the healing process, he once again subjected me to an exhaustive array of written questions and impersonal analysis to assess my symptoms. Hundreds of questions were asked, in different ways, to reveal some latent psychological obscurity. A difficult process for anyone on a good day. By the second appointment, I just wanted to get the hell out of there. A level of apprehension that is certain to be reflected in my answers. Obviously, my current cognitive state and anxiety will bias the outcome. Simply ask me how I feel – I will tell you, it's no mystery. There goes five grand down the toilet.

March 14, Year One

I feel most "normal" in the early mornings.

The sensations I've been experiencing these past several months con-
tinue to evolve and take on different shapes and textures. The cog-
nitive element is even more defined and ever-present. Ringing has
moved from a dull hum to a higher, piercing sensation. Movement
must mean change and that healing is taking place.

Five years in, DesignSight was on the decline. With the pop of
the dot-com bubble beginning in early '95, many of our clients and
projects dried up. The company was nearly acquired a couple of
times, but inquiries only led to dead ends. And as business opportunities eroded, so did our cash flow, and the agency soon became un-
sustainable. I was approved for a small-business loan for $112,000
to resurrect the firm. But in the eleventh hour, the lender revealed
that to secure the loan we needed to put our home up as collateral.
At this point, the risk became too great, and I opted not to sign.

Despite downsizing to a staff of three and relocating to a less
expensive office closer to our home, it became clear that it was time
to pull the plug. The most viable option for me (and Camille) was
to assume all debt and declare chapter seven. If our circumstances
had been different, and Camille and I weren't in the early stages of
starting a family, perhaps I would have raised the stakes and leveraged a little deeper to try and turn things around. But that wasn't
the case. We had a good run and a lot of fun while it lasted, but it
was time to move on.

Not to sound jaded, but the big winners in all this were the
IRS and the local and state tax beneficiaries who remained whole
throughout the entire process. We suffered, and they got paid. In
the end, we stuck American Express with a $30,000 balance and
broke the lease on a copy machine that only worked half the time.
We had to cut short our office lease midway – which they were,

fortunately, able to sublet within a few months to a company that produced hemp products – a new economy, a new era. It was a challenging time. But in hindsight, cutting our losses proved to be the best path forward.

By now, we had our first child, Liam, and I had discovered that my risk tolerance was far less than it once was. After DesignSight closed, I needed to something more stable to support our growing family. Against my nature and drive to go it alone, it became clear that it was time for me to put on my big-boy pants and get a "real job." But even then, I didn't anticipate what a long, arduous journey this would become. Given my desire for autonomy, I believed that one day something better would come along – better suited to who I was.

March 24, Year One

I've been in a state of melancholy for the past five months. It's only natural to want to feel more myself. There is an ebb and flow to it. Looking forward to a marked "window" to remind me of the wellness that lies ahead. I need this reassurance. It has been a few weeks since that last glimmer of lucidity. Must be patient.

April 1, Year One

Today the cognitive challenges are on full display. Problem-solving is proving difficult. My thinking is off, and my short-term memory is fragmented. Still having difficulty getting to the right word. The process of tracking my progress is slow and tedious but helps keep things in context. It's helpful to keep track of the ups and downs and identify patterns associated with what I'm doing (eating, exercise, sleep) to how I'm feeling. Work remains the biggest challenge.

April 8, Year One

I had a restless night, very poor sleep. Finally, feeling the trazodone bounce. I will see how the next couple of nights go.

Have been experiencing elevated agitation – felt it early this morning as "anxiety." Hopefully, this won't carry on for too many days. Just need to relax and accept this physical misfire as being part of the healing process.

My mom ran across a job opening at The Seattle Times. I applied right away. And, not so coincidentally, my dad had worked there for twenty years as a photo editor and was instrumental in advancing the quality of the paper. Under his tutelage, they began to earn national recognition, not least with a Pulitzer Prize. And apparently, he hadn't burned any bridges. The thought of his son entering the business was intriguing enough to persuade my future boss to take a risk on someone from outside the industry.

I began working at the Times in the early summer of '06. The transition was seamless and immediate. As soon as we closed the business, I took a brief vacation with the family, then dove headlong into my new role. However, going from a small design firm to a large company was a shock and took some adjustment. I was tasked with managing a staff of thirteen grumpy designers and one copywriter. They had recently come off a strike and had been without proper oversight for the better part of a year – during which a significant portion of the group had become disgruntled, and there was growing mistrust between coworkers. Despite having stepped into a difficult situation, I was excited to take on this new challenge. Because that's who I was – head down, stay the course, work hard.

One of my first tasks was to bring unity to the group. Through a process of team building, we made measurable improvements within the first few months. But some of the personalities were determined to not be happy with my presence since I hadn't properly earned my way into their ranks. We had some clashes, but the union contract made it difficult to take immediate action. Eventually, this took its toll. And after a few years, I was once again in search of something more fulfilling. And, by this point, most anything would do.

The Seattle Times taught me how to manage creative people in a complex and often contentious environment. And I did meet some capable and friendly people, especially among my peers. It must have been a rewarding place to work before the advent of the internet changed the way people got their news. People working together towards a common goal, committed to truth in journalism, less affected by outside influences.

The subsequent shift to online media crushed an industry that was otherwise trusted. There was a time when a story deemed newsworthy enough to make the paper meant something – it was credible. Today, due to a lack of industry standards and the marginalization of journalistic integrity, our news sources are a lot less reliable, and we're paying the price. Profit-driven enterprises sensationalize stories with biased points of view, resulting in shady facts. Cauterizing an audience already vulnerable to divisiveness and belligerent discourse.

Towards the middle of my nearly four-year tenure at the Times, I tried to make a move into the digital group, but my manager wasn't prepared to support the transition. Although she was an exceptional boss, she thought it more suiting that I remain at the helm of her department. Screw that; it was time to move on.

April 11, Year One

It's like living under several layers of blankets – occasionally one gets removed or replaced with another of different weight and texture.

April 14, Year One

Today was a challenging day. My focus was shot, and I had a difficult time tracking thoughts, ideas, and conversations. Is this the bottom? Can it get worse?

April 22, Year One

Had a large chocolate-chip cookie today – shouldn't have. But when things are consistently down, the little pleasures seem worth the risk. Still experiencing that modulating humming in my head – like a gas meter plugged into the back of my skull, reverberating a dull, constant trickle.

April 23, Year One

If you find yourself up to your knees in quicksand, having recently been up to your neck – you're still in quicksand. And being in quicksand is no fun at all.

ELEVEN

OUR LIFE OF ADVENTURE

Camille and I lived and played our way through the next few years. It was intense at first, spending virtually all our waking hours and nights together. I eventually graduated college and got my own living space. Swapping back and forth between each other's apartments, not quite cohabitating, and always leaving an escape route – which we seldom needed. We lived out each day, not looking too far ahead. Contract jobs for me, office stints, and waiting tables for her. Hanging out at various bars and music venues, the two of us together or with friends. We were inseparable (fig. 20, p.190).

Within a few short months of meeting one another, we made plans to travel to Europe, which we made good on the following summer. We crisscrossed a dozen or so countries from Russia to the southern tip of Italy. However, it wasn't a trip without challenges – my frantic moment lost in Saint Petersburg, getting on each other's nerves in Orleans that wicked ferry ride from Brindisi, and her run-in with ouzo in Greece.

April 24, Year One

There's a duality happening as I work to distinguish the symptoms of how I feel from who I am – the real me. My "wellness" center is still haywire. I often take a step back (within myself), to breathe and observe. To differentiate feelings and emotions from the phys-

ical discomforts that envelop me, which can otherwise cascade into emotional discomfort if left unchecked. Being able to recognize these differences helps lessen the burden. I must be my own observer to remain grounded.

April 26, Year One

The difficult bottom-line issue is that nobody knows or can empathize with how I feel. Kids are clueless – friends show concern yet can't imagine something that could take hold of someone for such an extended period – Camille still often wonders why I don't feel like socializing and gives me crap about it. If she only knew the moment-to-moment struggle I'm facing, she would refrain from remarking.

April 28, Year One

Terrible night's sleep. Thinking of everything. Couldn't relax. Challenging night. Guts will get me through the day. Nights like this make me question everything. Feeling like I'm going down the wrong path. Lots of negative thoughts and emotions.

And a tough day – but got some stuff done. Proves that if you face the day, no matter how difficult things may seem, you can work through it.

During our stay in Russia, we lived with Efim Shifrin – a kindred spirit my family and I had befriended the previous summer, hosting him as he participated in the Goodwill Games in Seattle. He was a renowned singer and actor in his homeland and had traveled to the US with the Russian athletes to entertain them during their stay.

Camille and I arrived just two months after the failed Soviet coup adding an air of uncertainty to our trip. We were very excited about the opportunity to visit a place few Westerners had ever seen and felt a sense of urgency to get in there before things potentially closed back up. We were apprehensive at first, mesmerized by the wars its citizens had endured over the centuries, eager to experience a culture so rich in history, yet not fully aware of the magnitude of economic and political transformation that was taking place right before our eyes.

Efim lived in a modest high-rise flat, located just outside Moscow, which he shared with his aunt and uncle, who raised him since childhood (fig. 21, p. 190). He greeted us with warmth and hospitality that eclipsed his own reception in Seattle, which was remarkable given the scarce resources available. We were humbled by the heroic lengths he went to put a bottle of Coca-Cola on the table and the look on his aunt's face when Camille took her first sip.

Accompanied by his personal bodyguard and driver, Efim showed us the city and its surrounding areas, including places we probably shouldn't have had access to – our travel visas were quite strict. Everywhere we went, people would point and giggle as they recognized Efim as he tried to move about unnoticed. And it didn't help that I was a six-five blond giant with a bright-red REI jacket cast against a backdrop of famine and deprivation. One evening, Camille and I attended a sold-out Russian performance in which Efim was the star attraction. What he said on stage to precipitate three thousand Russian people to clap in unison and turn their gaze our way ... we will never fully know.

After a week, Efim arranged for Camille and me to take a train to Saint Petersburg. He set us up in a vintage carriage, replete with wall-to-wall cherrywood finishes and a private sleeping cabin. The dutiful and intimidating Russian soldier collected our passports and tickets. We felt like fugitives, characters from another era, at the mercy of a foreign adversary.

It would be a long night, kept awake by the aging tracks and the fear that we'd never see those documents again (fig. 22, p. 190). We were met at the station by a trusted confidant who took exceptional care of us for those remaining few days. While in Saint Petersburg, we interacted with musicians, writers, and artists; enjoyed the beautiful architecture and scenery; and got to see and experience a culture that most can only imagine. And yet one surprisingly familiar to our own. We are a people cut from the same cloth, with the same fears and aspirations, longing to make a connection and enjoy a Coke together now and again.

Those two weeks in Russia were extraordinary for both Camille and me, and we're fortunate to have shared the experience together. It was an unforgettable first leg of our European journey. It was eye-opening and full of adventure – speeding across the lane-less freeway in a tiny black Lada, seeing first-hand what poor really looks like, while sharing fantastic meals with the rich and famous. It was a juxtaposition of the human experience and a visceral display of an imperfect civilization during a critical time of transition. In which decades of decay and an aging homeless population were intermingled with the tasks of everyday living. A walk from the flat to the sparsely stocked grocer meant having to step around destitute old women living off the streets as you made your way past the cabbie selling apples from the trunk of his car.

From Russia, we started things off with another sleepless night at a windowless hostel near Helsinki's Olympic stadium, which was undergoing a thorough renovation at ungodly hours. We learned how to get by on the appalling exchange rate in Stockholm, then took in the scenery as we journeyed by rail to Norway. There we stayed a few days with a college friend of mine who was living in Oslo with his new wife, attending art school, and contemplating starting a family. From there, we headed south to a lengthy stopover in Orléans, France, where we met up with a friend of Camille's, an exchange student that she and her family had hosted several years earlier.

Travel-weary after weeks confined to tight spaces, it is at this point we faced our first trial. With no place to go, we escaped to a quaint theater that happened to be playing The Wizard of Oz, subtitled in French. This was all we needed to remind ourselves of home and how far we'd come. We finished our trip heading south through Spain, then over to Sicily, before boarding an overnight ferry in rough seas to Greece, where we met an early snowfall, welcoming hospitality, and the best chicken dinner you could imagine.

[Throughout the healing process it was important for me to keep up my exercise. Running is something I enjoy and do regularly. Periodically, I'd write down what I thought to be satisfying running times.]

May 3, Year One

Big run – (14 miles) 1:44

I'm not sure how many more years we could have kept living like this, but from my perspective, it wasn't such a bad way to go. Her vision for what the future held was less ambiguous than mine. I was the wandering artist, sensitive and restless by nature, yet driven to do things my own way. She was more mature, grounded in values, determined to get on with things and move forward. After a few years came talk of commitment. It presented a conundrum for me:

a change that I wasn't sure I was ready to make. But also recognized as the natural next step for the both of us. It was time to "shit or get off the pot, " as Camille so eloquently likes to put things.

We got married on October 8, 1994, in an unpretentious, mid-century Catholic church located atop the north side of Seattle's Capitol Hill neighborhood (fig. 23, p. 190). We filled Saint Patrick's with about 120 guests, most from Camille's side of the family, many of whom had braved the trek from her hometown of Turton, South Dakota. We had a lively reception and closed the party down around eleven (I think they may have actually kicked us out). We arrived late at the Sorrento, a cozy upscale hotel where the bartender just happened to be, of all people, Suzanne. We continued our festivities until well after midnight, just like the night we met, minus the kitchen floor. We awoke the next day with sizable hangovers and discovered on the way out that I had left my wedding ring on the nightstand. One of many I would either misplace or leave behind over the years. Luckily, I retrieved that one, at least for a while.

Those first few years of marriage were packed full of adventure: partaking in weekend getaways, camping excursions, and summer road trips. Getting drunk and sleeping in; doing our own thing – just the two of us. These were freeing times. I was dabbling in art, she was socializing with friends, and together hosting parties and cookouts. After a while, Camille decided to go back to school to get her cosmetology license and pursue her dream of becoming a hairstylist, and I gave up the house-painting gig and got a job as a full-time graphic designer. Days were full and satisfying, with little stress. We lived pretty much for ourselves. A "do what we want, when we want" lifestyle, no strings attached. Kids would wait.

About six years into our marriage came talk of having children. We decided we wanted three and yet gave it only modest forethought. Despite our lack of fully developed career paths, we went for it anyway (fig. 24, p. 190). It would have been nice to have had a tighter financial handle on things, but where's the fun in that? Camille had a clearer sense of what she wanted to do, but I was still winging it as a young designer, less sure of myself, not really dialed in to where I was headed or how I intended to get there.

It's taken a couple decades for the realities of raising a family to catch up with me, the weight of the responsibility finally coming around to smack me upside the head. Fortunately, we saved where we could, stayed in one place, and for the most part, have remained employed. And we think we've gotten the kids through the critical child-rearing stages without causing too much damage – knock on wood. We have our home and our health, and we still have each other, but it hasn't been easy. In fact, I'd say for me, in light of the circumstances, it's gotten progressively more difficult.

May 12, Year One

Horrible night. Camille pulling away, can't blame her. Feeling like I'm back to square one. How can this be sustained?

May 20, Year One

It occurred to me that the mere thought and desire for sleep, especially in the early morning hours, often triggers an anxiety response. Need to break this cycle.

June 5, Year One

My primary issue right now is cognitive, a lack of lucidity, and the confidence that I normally have throughout the workday. This has been a great point of difficulty for me.

June 21, Year One

I ran the Seattle Rock and Roll half marathon – 1:38. I was pacing 1:35 but farted out with three miles to go.

More recently, I have felt insecure with who I am within this relationship, sharing in this life-long communion that I don't feel particularly worthy of being a part of much of the time. Yet somehow, it must be enough. Camille and I have faced real challenges while raising each other and the kids. And many couples have given up over much pettier things. But we carry on and forge ahead, despite my shortcomings. She stays with me regardless, and I, her. Probably for different reasons. Or maybe simply because we love each other and, in some cosmic way, cherish those infinitesimal odds of ever meeting, and who can forget that crazy entrance. As the days and years come and go, we work, we cry, we get angry, we love, we feel, we fail, we overcome, we wake up, and then we do it all over again. Why do we do this? And how did it all get so complicated and at the same time so easy? Perhaps I'll better understand it one day. But in the meantime, my gut tells me to keep pressing on, and trying, and praying, and learning – and that I am so fortunate.

I find this whole life of mine to be quite surreal. The older I get, the more unreal it becomes. I don't know if this is self-realization, transformation, or a rite of passage to that next phase in life, but the further along I go, the stranger things seem – it's not a bad thing, just kind of unexpected.

September 16, Year One

I woke up in the middle of the night experiencing an adrenaline rush, and my mind over-run with anxious, frivolous thoughts. This is nothing to worry about, as it will correct itself over time. My body requires time to heal.

It's normal to feel frustrated when awoken, but there is no need to spend time worrying about random thoughts. Concerns that may not be real anyway and only lead to frustration and additional stress. It's best to remind myself of all that is good.

Here's a list of positive things that are real and happening in my life right now:

I'm well into a healing process that will eventually lead me to feel better than I've felt in a long time

Right now, I'm doing relatively well in my job, and there's no reason I will not continue to perform this way, whether in my current position or somewhere else

I've got a great family that's healthy and loves me

I'm still able to do and enjoy many things such as attending the kid's sports activities, running, watching movies, having dates with Camille, eating … the list is endless

Now it's time to rest and let my thoughts wander among all the other good things that await me.

The way she holds her fork, that subtle look on her brow, those otherwise imperceptible nuances. As time passes, I find myself staring more and more into the shadow of the man himself. As if he's returned with a shotgun in hand to say, "Hey, stay away from my daughter!" Our love cannot exist without depth, and yet I find myself treading water at times, skimming the surface – yearning to be locked in that youthful dance forever. I know it doesn't work that way, but this is the way of things as we get older – the aches and pains, my loud chewing, and those genetic carryovers – little reminders that we are ever-changing. I need the courage to release myself to the depths of what we've worked so hard to achieve and accept the inevitable. I need to let go and reveal myself to us and have faith in the process.

Camille is one of the most beautiful people I have ever met, inside and out. She's everything you might expect from a daughter of a loving and hardworking family of faith, raised on small-town values (fig. 25, p. 191). Rich in heart with a humongous zest for life, what you see is what you get. She can be heavy-handed and unforgiving, and sometimes wrong, but always honest and true. Her spirit burns bright on those around her, and no one would dispute the level of energy she brings to a room and the thrill when its focus is placed solely on you. She's imperfect, she doesn't care, and at the same time, she's deeply caring. She's persevering, relentless, and the perfect complement to balance out my own insecurities. She's all I could ever have imagined in a life partner.

[I ran across an online chat room of people who were having (or had) similar experiences related to benzodiazepine withdrawal. I joined the group briefly and was surprised to see thousands sharing similar stories of discomfort and pain related to withdrawal and recovery. Everyday people – fathers, mothers, daughters, sons – who, not unlike myself, were prescribed a drug to treat something relatively benign. Some got off it quickly and were having issues, others were taking it slower and still struggling. For the most part, they had been cast aside with little support from their doctor, having to figure things out on their own. Below is one of a few blogs I wrote to gain outside affirmation that I wasn't alone in what I was experiencing.]

September 22, Year One, Blog Post

Those who have successfully made their way through this process, I'd welcome words of encouragement. Nobody in my "real-world" community has been able to explain what I'm up against, let alone relate to what I've been going through. Is there light at the end of the tunnel? What are some reasonable expectations? Or is the key to having none?

Sept 29, Year One, Blog Post

Thanks. Over the last several months, the texture of this affliction has shifted for me as well. The first few months were really about survival. Dealing with an overwhelming sense that my head was compressed, and my thinking muddled. For the first few months, it was easier to cope because the symptoms made sense and were expected. But now, although I'm functioning at a higher level, it's even more challenging because time is pushing this ever closer to the realm of implausibility – you can't help but wonder whether this will continue with no end.

TWELVE

The Back Story

It was late summer of '13 we had once again slogged our way by RV to Camille's parents' home in South Dakota, a three-acre spread located between two tiny farm towns, about four miles (or a thirty-minute run) due east of Turton. It's a modest homestead, surrounded by rough grass and a few dozen trees, near where two highways intersect. Offering order and stability in an area otherwise exposed to unpredictable and often extreme weather conditions – an oasis amid square miles of pancake-flat farmland as far as the eye can see. This had become our annual family-road-trip destination for the past twenty years. And, in many respects, a place of refuge (fig. 26, p. 191).

In its heyday, Turton was an essential stop-over for the railroad and the epicenter of a thriving farming community. Today, it's made up of a bank and a post office, a few family-owned farms, and an unyielding spirit that embodies hard work and Midwestern values. Only a few dozen homes remain, many of which are tattered and empty. But Turton has escaped the fate of most agricultural towns its size (fig. 27, 28, p. 191). Communities succumbing to the re-distribution of industry, leaving behind remnants of their former selves: crumbled reminders of a way of life long abandoned by an irrelevant railway and the promise of a more prosperous future.

Shortly after we arrived, we and Camille's immediate family, along with dozens of other cousins and uncles, their families, and friends, converged on Sioux Falls to attend a wedding for one of

Camille's nieces. As I prepared for bed that first evening at the hotel, I realized I had left my medication back at the in-laws. Thinking little of it, I settled in for the night. However, as the hours passed, I began to experience more pronounced levels of anxiety, as well as the emergence of a rushing sensation in my head. As the night crawled onward, I began to suspect a correlation between the prescription I was taking and the symptoms that I was now experiencing.

The next day, having been kept awake virtually all night by the escalating symptoms, I was in no shape to partake in the day's festivities. My brain needed the medication simply to undo what I was experiencing – anxiety beyond anything I had felt before. The only solution for me at this point was to bow out, leave Camille behind with the kids, and make the three-hour trek back to her parents' house. After I arrived and within a couple of hours of taking my prescription, my theory proved correct, and things began to settle down to relative normalcy. Apparently, a milligram of alprazolam was all I needed to calm my agitated state.

Once we got back to Seattle, I was determined to address the adverse effects the medication was having on my health. My doctor and I worked out a plan to wean me off "safely" and thus began my journey towards wellness – little did I know. I also signed up and participated in a mindfulness training program and sought additional support with a therapist to better prepare myself for what lay ahead.

While I was incrementally reducing my dosage, I was not sleeping well and decided to move to the downstairs bedroom. I was restless and exhausted and felt that sleeping separate for now was the best solution for the both of us, although Camille could sleep through most anything. My thinking and cognition were also affected, and I felt incredibly groggy during most of my waking hours.

During the final weeks of lowering the dosage, as I would drift in and out of sleep at night, I would hallucinate periodically. Weird perceptual oddities that would jar me awake. The lights from the

ceiling-mounted fire alarm would cast messages onto the floor –
only to be lost as I went in for a closer look. And strange night-time
visitors and nightmares conspired to ratchet up the anxiety that I
was already experiencing – a relentless series of unsettling events,
enough to make me question my own sanity.

One of these episodes stood out as implausible and, at the same
time, very real. Suggesting the subconscious and conscious realms
may be more connected than we might think. It was an experience
made even more strange given the timing – registering so clear
during one of the most unstable and vulnerable periods in my life.

October 1, Year One

*During my tolerance months, my cognitive capacity was diminish-
ing. However, I experienced an immediate and undeniable esca-
lation in symptoms at the point when I jumped off the drug altogether. And these effects have been hanging on for the better part of
eleven months.*

*The following symptoms result in an overarching sense of not feel-
ing at ease within myself, mired in periodic changes in mood, and a
sense of heightened vulnerability that didn't exist before coming off
the drug – or before taking it.*

*Perception: Looking at the world as if there's a veiled filter en-
cumbering my ability to take it all in: a closing in or compressed
perception resulting in an uneasy quality, feeling detached from
my surroundings. Periodic visual jerky movements as I scan my
surroundings, heightened sensitivity to light. A lack of fluidity and
diminished connection with my environment.*

*Thinking: Reading comprehension is slower. Have a terrible time
taking and following directions. Writing and articulating ideas co-
gently and linearly is more of a chore. The more demands I put on*

my brain, the more I feel that sense of cognitive compression.

Conversations: Do OK with light banter but get lost easily in conversations that are more demanding and require a train of thought. Anything that requires analyzing or probing beneath the surface is still a challenge.

Hallucinations and nightmares: Awake periodically during the night to decipher messages cast onto the walls and floor. Disturbing faces jar me awake. The sense that the walls are cavernous, sometimes moving, or that I've somehow been transported to another place.

Memory: My short-term memory is choppy. Most things get through, but it's not as accessible as it once was. Time and chronology are messed up, and it's difficult for me to recall what I did that morning or past weekend; I must work at it.

Hissing: I've best described this as if my brain were equipped with a natural gas line, hearing the rush of high-pitched compressed air traveling through my head, more so at certain times of the day but always present. I sense that when this "hissing" goes away, I will be healed. It's like I can hear the damaged receptors misfiring in my head.

Physical: Fluctuation of an arbitrary stress response, resulting in disturbed sleep, not necessarily tied to thought. A light, tingly sensation of adrenaline flushing out from the feet up. Periodic hot flushes at night coupled with waves of stress. My eyes feel like cotton balls, and I've had tension headaches in the past – these have lessened.

THIRTEEN

Who Is This Guy?

It was a Saturday, and I had been tossing, turning, and sweating much of the night. The less alprazolam I took, the more restless and agitated I got. Apparently, I was experiencing a rebound reaction, in which a drug intended to calm the senses takes on opposing characteristics. Although exhausted, I was optimistic, knowing that I was finally on a path to getting this substance out of my system. I could sense the finish line; the end was in sight, and I knew I'd soon be rid of the drug.

Sunday morning finally arrived. I was still drifting in and out of sleep and was pretty much exhausted – a sensation I had unfortunately grown accustomed to. It was then that I had an odd lucid dream involving a classmate of mine from college. A relatively inconsequential figure during the two years I lived at the fraternity – when art classes and friendships from outside the house occupied most of my time. Nevertheless, it resonated crystal clear, playing out in high-def as I lay there half-awake, half-dead, standing out amidst the garbled mess of dreams that had preceded it.

It was exceptionally vivid yet progressively confusing as I began to orient myself to the waking world – like when I'd catch myself trying to decipher those messages on the floor (I swear, they were there). The recollection was random and insignificant. But I could see his face so clearly. So much so that I think I even tried to touch it. But I couldn't recall his name for the life of me! I knew him well enough and remembered exactly where our lives had crossed decades earlier – we were casual roommates for a Semester at WSU. It had been twenty-eight years since I'd last seen him, and I hadn't thought of him since. Why now? A nice enough guy, just a random memory, I guess.

Even if I'm dead-to-the-world tired, there's something about a run that brings me back around: it fuels me. Running affords me time to do something healthy for my body. It allows my thoughts to wander and my anxieties to drift away. And despite how poorly I felt, this morning would be no exception. I laced up my shoes and headed out the door.

Within a few minutes, I had descended the long hill a few blocks from my home, as I'd done a thousand times before, the ground leveling out as I reached the High School off to my left. It was then I spotted a car outside of my peripheral, coming from the opposite direction, approaching at the appropriate speed. It slowed slightly, despite me running well off to the side – a random pedestrian-jogger blending in with his surroundings – a mere speck amongst specks. Then the driver-side window rolled down just enough for a head to pop out to grab my attention. As if right on cue, a voice rang out, "Hey Chris, it's Bill!" He smiled, rolled up the window, and drove off.

October 5, Year One

It's Sunday, 11:00 pm, and I can tell that I'm in a negative feedback loop. My anxiety level is high. I can feel it in my chest. My mind is emanating anxiety from nowhere. Thoughts are spinning. And I don't know why because there is no specific topic or worry. It just seems to be bearing down on me for no reason. Must weather it. God, please provide me with an end to this soon.

November 9, Year Two

14.5 (miles) 1:48

December 11, Year Two

Overall, looking back on the previous year, I'm doing better for sure. I'm feeling more connected to people in conversation, and my ability to think deeper has improved. My capacity to do more at work has also increased. Month-to-month progress, however, is still difficult to gauge because the changes have been so subtle. Still, work to do.

FOURTEEN

That Dang Cat

I really enjoy running the rural highways when we visit Turton: endless stretches of road to chase down my innermost thoughts, a welcome respite from everyday life back home.

The weight of the wind, pressing from the front or pushing from behind – makes all the difference, depending on which direction you're headed. The sounds of the birds as they lay nesting in the ditches and the spook of pheasants as I cross over the culverts – I can't tell who's more startled. The smell of freshly cut hay resting in the sun and that heavy air as it makes its way through the baking soil. To be surrounded by nature in this way motivates me to stay in motion. To participate in its dance and take in its fragrance is a privilege. Seldom do I stop, if only to keep the proliferation of mosquitoes from having their way.

As I trek past fields of sunflowers, corn, beans, and swaths of prairie grass separated by shelterbelts and farms stitched together by miles of barbed wire, I find myself lost within these landscapes, as if I were a part of them. I imagine what it must have been like long before the barriers were put in place: herds of bison peppering the horizon, less structure to the land. It's easy to envision as you squint to shield against the sun, taking in this impressionistic view. My senses attune, living the moments, time serving little purpose. To test my grit in the presence of nature brings its own reward. To be in harmony with the land in this way is a gift.

I was somewhere between two small towns delineated by quarters of crops and untilled land for reserve – the solace marred only by my breathing and the water sloshing around in my crinkly plastic bottle. Twenty minutes in, and I could already feel its contents heating up in my hand. The nearest place of refuge – a couple of miles away. Civilization identifiable only by tiny dots on the horizon, telephone poles, and a string of wire on either side of the road. The only element that could not be contained that morning – or so I thought – was the breeze, carrying with it the aroma of the land and the chirpings of nestlings as I passed by (see cover image).

As I made my way alongside the narrow highway, I was met with the intermittent whiff of cow dung and the occasional stench of roadkill – pungent but quick to pass. I was just beginning to settle into my rhythm when I was startled by an unusual sound – the squeak of a kitten as it popped its head up from the grassy ditch just a few yards ahead. He was waiting, as I was certain to be the only human to have passed by on foot since the last time I came through a year ago. He immediately scampered towards me, at which point I paused. But, feeling the onset of the elements and nearing the second leg of my run, I had little desire to deal with a feral cat. So off I went.

He would have none of it. He flanked me and got right up under my feet as I attempted to regain my pace. I stumbled to avoid stepping on him. He was a dusty orange tabby with white paws and couldn't have been more than a couple weeks old. He seemed in remarkably good condition if a bit emaciated. How he ended up here, in the middle of nowhere, was baffling. But here he was, on his solo mission, escaping from God knows what, determined to follow me straight down the middle of the highway.

I'd put about thirty yards between us when I made that fatal mistake – I glanced back. It was over – for the both of us. Having reached the end of what would prove to be the last leg of his journey flopped over onto the pavement, exhausted. When I picked him up, he was working hard to stay with me. His little chest heaving, I could see his heart pounding through his translucent skin. His eyes were half-closed and hazy, like a person dying, staring wistfully up into the sky. I was able to drip a few drops of water into his mouth, and within a minute, he came around and opened his eyes. At which point, I'd imprinted on him. And he on me – as the years would reveal. Then I made an about-face and began the long, sweaty walk back to the house. What the hell. They're only mosquitoes.

Little did I understand the impact he would have on our lives: a lonely wanderer finding his way out of a ditch to enter our world so unexpectedly. The odds of it happening at all were silly, like a lightning bolt striking the ground to set the field ablaze, scorching the land and rejuvenating the soil over time. But over the years, that lightning strike would nurture our family in more ways than I could ever have imagined.

January 27, Year Two

It's 2:30 am. I've awakened once again with a rush of adrenaline. I fear that I will not be able to go back to sleep. The fear is irrational yet implanted. I'll experience a hot flush, and the thoughts follow. It has a post-traumatic quality, deep-seated, creeping in from out of the blue – yet I have no history of anything that would cause such a reaction. Not sure if it's related to dysregulation of my nervous system or if it's just fear-based. So, I acknowledge it here tonight and invite it to leave.

A newborn, two toddlers, a kitten, and a fueling mishap in Jackson Hole challenged Camille to her wit's ends. While I spent the better part of the day unraveling my mistake at the pump, she spent the entire afternoon in a hotel lobby juggling the troupe, wondering if and when I would ever come back. We did make it home a few days later, hobbling in on fumes with the aptly named latest addition to our family, Dakota, with only hours to spare before I started my new job at The Seattle Times.

Several months passed as Dakota adapted to his new life in the big city. It didn't take long before we realized that there was no keeping him indoors – you can take the cat out of the farm ... Just shy of a year after he arrived, he waddled home one afternoon seemingly out of sorts. He had clearly been injured, but to what extent we could not immediately tell. He wasn't in much pain, but he was struggling to breathe. I had seen the signs before but knew it would take more than a few drops of water to revive him this time around.

We took him to the neighborhood vet to be examined. An x-ray revealed that his diaphragm had been ruptured, enabling his vital organs to move up into his chest cavity – an injury most likely due to blunt-force trauma to his abdominal region. He had been struck by a car. We were faced with a complicated and costly procedure to save his life, with only a marginal chance of survival. The vet recommended we take him to a better equipped surgical center for the operation and cautioned that it would be expensive. We told him that this was something we didn't think we could afford. Then he made us an offer.

"I'll tell you what," he said, "I'll do the procedure regardless. If he survives, you can pay me significantly less than the surgical center would charge and take him home. And if you can't afford that, I'll keep him, because Dakota's just a really special cat." We couldn't refuse. We paid him the eight-hundred bucks.

Dakota belonged to the neighborhood. No matter who you were, he had a way of ingratiating himself into your life. Those he would visit grew accustomed to his friendly demeanor and openly welcomed him into their homes for a visit or a snack – he was the best-fed cat around. People enjoyed him because he was respectful and quick to return a purr.

Several years ago, a local Realtor told me the story of how he helped close the sale during an open house. Dakota had apparently found his way into the home and helped himself to one of the beds, where he proceeded to take a nap. Our soon-to-be neighbor commented on how that cat made the whole house feel warm and inviting. "A positive omen," she would later say, persuading them to join our community and sealing the deal. The Realtor didn't have the heart to tell them that the cat didn't belong to the homeowners and that he'd simply wandered in off the street. Just like he had wandered into our lives a few years earlier.

I'd gently rest my ear against his side, taking in the rhythmic sounds of his heart, wondering how he could sustain that tempo for much longer. Listening to the vibrations of his purr in exchange for the warmth of my head resting softly against his body embodied the essence of living itself. If he wasn't strolling around the neighborhood, I knew exactly where to find him. Despite numerous rooms, three floors, and plenty of couches and nooks in which to hide and sleep, there he'd be, curled up right where I slept, sunken into the top cover. I see him now as I did that first morning when I gingerly lifted him off the highway and held him in the palm of my hand – looking up at me, forever connected (fig. 29, p. 191).

January 29, Year Two

It's late and time to relax and let it all go. Let anxiety flow out of the body and for the mind to seek calm. Allow the body to float, be still, and join the quietness of the resting world. Be calm, be safe. No worry is worth lugging around into this time of sanctuary. Take in the stillness and allow the body naturally to seek what it desires. Rest.

March 5, Year Two

I remember several months back looking forward to a time when I could share my own "recovery" success with others, maybe even be a source of inspiration as they too continued to wait it out. I'm not there yet. It helps to put it out there because I have yet to meet anyone in person who's been through a similar experience. I'd like to be that person for someone one day.

Looking back on the year, I recall being in a state of "survival mode," wondering how I would make it through the day, the week, let alone retain my job. Now happy to report it's not as much of a crisis as it once was, as I am relatively functional and able to manage the trailing symptoms. I am still dealing with disturbed sleep patterns and what would otherwise be considered "low-grade" generalized anxiety, as well as head fog, cognitive slowness, challenges with simple directions, and my vision is blurry. But I seem to be moving in the right direction. And, I'm still employed, thankfully.

FIFTEEN

THE HOUSE I BUILT

Like my mom, I've always been a doer. Compelled, even obsessed at times to complete a task. That's not to say I'm proficient at
everything, but when I do set my mind to something, I become hyper-focused, often sacrificing time with family and friends to reach
an end goal, whatever that might be – opting to stay on a mission
over taking a break to relax, recharge, and engage. It's not enough
to desire an outcome; you've got to throw yourself all in to make it
happen.

I like to build and tinker. To plot out ideas and see them come
to life. I took a few woodshop classes in middle and high school,
which further stoked my interest. There's something visceral about
the whole process. The feel of the tools and materials in my hands,
the taste and smell of freshly cut wood, and the finished surface as
I brush away the powdery residue – the tackiness of the glue on my
fingertips and that sense of satisfaction as I step back to observe its
final form. It's gratifying to create something from nothing and see
its place and utility in this world. From backyard tree forts to odd
projects and repairs around the house, I've always been drawn to
working with my hands (fig. 30, p. 191). But the real prize awaited
me – to one day design and build a space that we could live in as a
family.

We bought our home in 1997 in a quiet little neighborhood just
ten minutes north of downtown Seattle for a hundred and forty
thousand dollars after renting it for three years (fig. 31, p. 191).

Wedgwood is a friendly and non-pretentious middle-class community, where backyards are spacious and tall firs and maples line the streets amid undulating hills and hidden streams. I put fifteen thousand down to secure the loan, from the money I earned painting houses and the rise and splitting of Microsoft stock. Katsu, our landlord (a banker by profession), generously carried the note for a couple of years (at 8 percent) until we were ready to transfer the title. No bank would have lent us the money initially. We were just too transient in our careers.

Shortly after we purchased the home, I decided our sloping backyard needed a little leveling, which set in motion a series of home improvement projects that would busy our lives for years to come. Since we didn't have a basement, I reasoned that we should simply take the dirt out from under the house and spread it across the yard. After moving dozens of cubic yards of compact soil with five-gallon buckets and dumping it into our backyard, we then had a nicely terraced yard. Problem solved. Except, we now had a giant cavern under the house that needed attention (fig. 32, p. 191).

The concrete pour took longer than anticipated. Tarps and French drains kept most of the water out, but it wasn't without incident. At the height of the rainy season, we were periodically woken by the unmistakable thud of heavy, wet soil hitting the ground. Luckily, the cave-in never happened, but there were definitely moments when I questioned whether I had gotten myself too far in over my head. It was December of '98 when we got the new foundation in place, and our precariously situated house was secure at last. The excavation and retrofit took about a year, plus another year to make it livable, just in time for the arrival of our son Liam.

As our family grew to five, despite our new basement, our living space had become constrained. Our youngest, Ruby, was just shy of two and beginning to get around. We loved the location, had discovered that our school cluster was top-notch, and got along well with the neighbors. For those reasons, we resolved to stay put. And felt our best option was to go up, to add a third level. I also thought that the sooner we got started, the better because the kids would be ever more demanding of our time as they got older (like they weren't already). Plus, since all three were shacking up in the drafty old garage, which I'd hastily converted into an office several years earlier, then a bedroom, we could use the space. It's amazing the stories we create to rationalize a need to move forward with an agenda. Thus began the big build in the winter of 2003.

I'd spent the better part of a year preparing, designing, budgeting, and approving plans with the city. By year two, I was ready to start building. Since I didn't completely understand what I was doing, I thought it would be practical if I constructed the second-floor walls on the ground in my newly terraced backyard – like building my own giant Lego set. A similar process Scott and I rehearsed as children many times over – only to a much grander scale. This approach worked out well. Within a few months, I had most of the sections completed, numbered, stacked, and ready for assembly.

In the summer, I removed the existing roof in one afternoon. And, with the help of family and friends, began laying the subfloor the following morning. Within a couple of long days, Brent and I hoisted the sections up to the third floor and into place, forming the walls and rooms and what would provide the base for the attic and roof, which would contain a fourth-story studio – a place where I would eventually write much of this book. The entire process: from removing the old roof, roughing in a third level, and installing the new roof, took about two weeks. And I believe it only rained once (fig. 33, p. 192). Things had gone relatively smoothly up to this point: head down, stay the course.

March 8, Year Two

It's the middle of the night, and I am awake with anxiety and random thoughts. I invite my worries to leave my body. Stress and anxiety associated with work, family, and feelings have no place in these resting hours. May they leave me in peace.

The time I spent working on the house was rough on Camille. The second half of the project was difficult for all of us but especially her. My argument that the kids were "less mobile" as the rationale for moving forward was ill-conceived. The added weight and responsibility that fell on her to pick up the slack in the evenings and weekends took its toll. Alcohol became her coping mechanism.

It progressively became clear that she needed help. She was aware of this and began contemplating steps to do something about it. But at this point, I felt it wasn't for me to insist on immediate change. Sensing her resolve, I believed she needed the space to find her own way.

Camille remained in South Dakota with the kids for a few weeks that summer while I stayed behind and continued to work feverishly on the house. Though sick, she was with her family and had their full support, and the kids were well cared for too. Upon returning to Seattle, she entered a rehab facility for about six weeks while my manager's college-age daughter watched the kids, and I went off to work. We were fortunate that I had a compassionate boss whose early memories of her father were of how he struggled with alcoholism and the toll it took on her own family. She wanted to support us if we were willing to do the work necessary to heal ourselves. She could have just as easily looked the other way.

Camille did put in the work, got healthy, and came home. And, fortunately, the home project was nearing completion. Within a few months, we moved upstairs and began to enjoy our new living space. It was a huge relief to finally have this episode of our life behind us, and we looked forward to starting anew.

As I added the final touches to the upstairs bathroom, weary with fatigue and with one last swipe of grout, I sank back, exhaled, and sobbed with relief. It was my first stopping point in over a year: the house was complete.

March 17, Year Two

It's been up and down lately. Need to be on the lookout for "worry." Sixteen months and the realization of feeling better eludes me. Need to keep my spirits up as I encounter bumps. Hope and vision are important, but I must be careful not to put too much into a recovery timeline – missed expectations lead to letdowns as the weeks/ months come and go. Can't imagine anyone not doubting themselves or the process given the duration. Will this ever let up? Will I one day experience my normal imperfect self?

SIXTEEN

WHAT'S NEXT?

It never occurred to me that the latter years would be so dang tough. I don't know if this is attributable to a "mid-life crisis" or whether something in me just gave way, but forty-plus has been a bitch! And dealing with my recent health debacle hasn't helped. I realize I have it better than most and have lived a blessed life, but that privilege has yet to translate into comfort, belonging, purpose, and self-assurance. On the contrary, I feel as unsure of myself as ever. I wonder if I've been looking for resolve in all the wrong places. Expecting "something" out of the process of my life, rather than pausing to cherish life's day-to-day moments more fully as they happen. Or whether something's just wrong with me – that I'm at the start of some sort of mental decline. Nevertheless, these years have revealed that for whatever reason, I'm not living contentedly.

However, something in me offers clues, a calling to look at the world differently, albeit through a lens of discomfort. Suggesting that perhaps my way of thinking, how I saw myself fitting in, was too reliant upon a prescriptive view, distracting me from living my true and immediate self. I don't really know what this all means, but maybe it's a start towards something less expectation-driven and more aligned with how I ought to be living my life. I just hope that I'm around long enough to see how it all plays out.

March 18, Year Two

A wave of dread and a sense of foreboding came over me this after-noon like never before. Very acute sensations. I felt a sinking feeling in my chest which kept me awake most of the night. This seems to have no rhyme or reason. There's a lot going on with work, the uncertainty of employment, but nothing too unexpected. I recently developed a ninety-day personal plan to map out my thoughts and set some goals. But, despite my proactive planning, today was scary emotionally. Unsettling and depressing feelings came up abruptly and caused me great physical and emotional discomfort. Scary not knowing what's causing this. Feels out of control. Not sure how long I can endure. I pray for relief soon.

My time has come for peace, healing, and wellness. I demand this – have worked at this for so long. Time for rest.

There's a young woman who has shown up in my dreams for as long as I can remember. She's beautiful and loving, and yet her appearance changes. I do not know her, nor do I believe we've ever met, and yet there's something familiar about her. The encounters invoke a sense of feeling loved, in love, and safe. And when I wake, I feel abandoned, as if something has been taken away – a similar feeling to the one I experienced when I left Chicago. Upon waking, I feel a profound sense of loss and sadness. I wonder if she's trying to communicate something – a soul that I once knew and was close to, from a past life or something, reaching out to connect. If this is the case, I would ask for release, because at this point, I don't under-stand what is to be gained. But if she's merely an aberration lodged in my subconscious, I think it's time for her to move on. How can I raise my children in a healthy and meaningful way if I cannot let go of my past self? How can I love fully if I'm distracted by feelings of discontent?

March 26, Year Two

Tough period of late. Sleep last night was poor. Agitation and work stress are high. The duration of this whole experience has left me with a sense of permanence, which is a very daunting prospect. If I could check out for a year and take care of myself, it would help minimize the stress. But this isn't realistic. And I certainly don't want to inflict this upon my family. Need to keep finding the inner strength, protect myself as best I can, have faith that this will get better soon, and gut it out.

March 30, Year Two

Generally, the beginning of the week brings with it added tension and a mixed mood – today would be no exception. I'll consider myself "over this" when I don't think about it as much. I think about it often because the symptoms are a constant reminder that something is not right. Lately, I've been consciously aware of the symptoms maybe 70 percent of the time, my hope would be that a year from now that is closer to 30 percent. I could live with that. Completely gone and forgotten would be preferred. Also, that my life with Camille is back to a healthier pattern – that we're sleeping together more regularly, and I can be more giving in the relationship. And that my memory and focus are essentially restored.

I have found the demands of raising a family to be at odds with my desire to fully discover and explore my ambitions. These are not inseparable in the grand scheme of things, but my aspirations have yet to be adequately satisfied. And, as selfish as this may seem, I have found the responsibility of raising a family to conflict at times with my ability to realize personal gratification – unless I've just been going about it all wrong.

Whatever I happen to be doing never seems to be enough – to satisfy that sense of need. The idea of meaningful work is an abstract thought, a moving target, morphing into the next best thing – a worldly concept incapable of delivering the fulfillment for which I've been longing. And, in recognizing this have reconciled finding meaning in what I do with the way I live my life. I hope the questions I ask as a result will reveal within me a purpose that has been so elusive. And in doing so, lead to a more harmonious second act.

I'm a carefree person by nature. A spirit content to observe from afar, alas having graduated into the role of breadwinner, within an uber-competitive, take-no-prisoners society. On the one hand, I'm a self-absorbed introvert, and on the other, I'm relied on to provide physical and emotional sustenance so that others may feel safe and loved and flourish. Fast-forward fifteen years, in a job that has become stagnant, realizing the most sensible course of action is to stay the course and ride it out – because there's too much risk in disrupting the family plan to chase delusions of grandeur. But at the same time, I feel there's a reward ahead, one of patience and sacrifice. Like the satisfaction of having reached the end of a long race. And that one day soon, by simply contemplating the question, "why?" this will all make more sense.

I can't help but think of those artists you hear about who say they would die if they didn't have their craft, their music, or whatever it was that "saved" them. It's a worn-out cliché. Only the fortunate few can romanticize about their own road to success, skimming over the fact that luck and timing had as much to do with it as anything. Sure, it takes effort, but never overlook where you came from, how you got there, and who helped you along the way, nor allow yourself to be distracted from what's truly important.

Creative types who can't fully invest in their own singular path won't die. They just have to find another way. We all must change, adapt, and evolve towards what really matters to us. The art is in the struggle, and the spoils are there for those willing to face the challenge and do the work necessary to discover their true essence, their own creation.

April 6, Year Two

At this point, I can't help but second-guess whether how I feel today is related to what happened almost a year and a half ago. Looking for some encouragement. Does this ever get better? Will the day when this thing is behind me ever come? So tough when you're in the middle of it.

April 27, Year Two

Depression is lurking. Sometimes it pokes its head out and tricks me into thinking that my life is not abundant with goodness and hope. I forget how normal feels. I cannot help but wonder if getting back to that place is more wishful thinking than anything. I know what it feels like to be well. It is reasonable to expect that feeling well should be what I'm experiencing most of the time since that has been my natural state for most of my life. All I can do is accept how I feel today and continue doing the things that are conducive to healing and wellness.

I question my capacity and desire to commit to another person's aspirations at this point in my life, especially given my line of work, my current state of mind, and, frankly, attitude. I mean, if I made a change, I don't know how I could muster the strength to begin to care. A career move today would presumably result in a step back in pay, which would negatively impact my family, something I'd like to avoid if at all possible – it would have to be a role of a higher purpose.

We've been financially skating by these past several years – spending more than saving, determined to keep the kids active and our lifestyle in motion. Fortunately, we saved early and have equity in our home. Nonetheless, with the prospect of college looming and the need to maintain a household in a costly city, the thought of making a career change now seems daunting. The irony is that I've always felt in control of my employment trajectory: open to new opportunities better suited to my nature and interests, eager to pounce when the right moment presented itself. Maybe it's an age thing, or I'm still reeling from the effects of my health crisis, or simply bad timing, but things just haven't worked out as I'd envisioned. I'm not sure what I've got left in the tank if something were to materialize or how I would handle it if I found myself in the unfortunate situation of having to start over. This is new territory for me. Because up to this point, I've always been a go-getter.

May 5, Year Two

Sunday evening, Monday, and part of Tuesday were a slog. It was tough to focus – today was a back-to-square-one kind of day. Lots of work-related stress with layoffs looming, downsizing the agency, and inevitable change on the horizon. Fear of being unemployed for any period – keep the faith – things will work out.

May 16, Year Two

Although I prefer not to dwell, it's important to articulate how I feel on these difficult days. It must be overstimulation that's adding to the cognitive confusion – I'm just plain feeling disconnected. The day started out OK, then quickly got tough. Depression seeped in quickly. Sleep has been a challenge and tracking days is difficult. Feeling bad that Camille and I are not in sync and that she's not getting my full self. These days I question where this is going or if this has turned into something different – a real mental illness. Feels like I'm giving it all I've got and have little to show for it. I ask that this resolves soon, please.

SEVENTEEN

CHASING PURPOSE

Over the years, I've looked into a variety of design-related jobs. On several occasions, I got close to what might be considered "choice" positions. But they never quite panned out. And I wouldn't say I was a confident interviewee either. I'd get nervous answering questions, too many scenarios running through my head all at once. Or maybe they'd sense that "go it alone" vibe, realizing I was more intent on pursuing my own path than buying into the program they had to offer.

I had an entry-level job opportunity right out of college to design computer-interface icons for Microsoft. It suited my skill set well and would have put me on a lucrative career path. Going into the interview, I knew that the hiring manager had a fine arts background. My two additional years of art at WSU, as well as dual art degrees from the UW, were certain to set me apart from the other candidates.

To leverage this inside track and strengthen my presentation, I included a few paintings and drawings of my own. I felt it would be advantageous to showcase my diverse creative skillset. The interviewer said that she appreciated my artwork, that she missed watercolor painting herself, and that she had gotten her first job at Microsoft without having any previous design education. She was sure to see the value I would bring to the group and that my broad understanding of color and composition and solid foundation for graphic design would be an invaluable asset to the team. But I also got the sense that being an artist was a path she wished she had pursued.

Even with all those perceived advantages, I didn't get the job. It's unfortunate because I know I would have done well in that role. Maybe the manager thought she was doing me a favor, encouraging me to pursue a direction that "clearly" suited me, one that eluded her – that of being a fine artist. I didn't consider that displaying my talent in this way would backfire when entering the workforce. Several of my peers seized on these early opportunities, and I witnessed the positive impact working at a company such as Microsoft had on their careers. I envied the huge leg-up it afforded them and the many open doors that followed.

May 17, Year Two

The duration is weighing heavily on our marriage and family life. I feel terrible about all of this. It has held hostage what intimacy we had. Which only adds more weight to my stress load. Combined with the work pressures, which by any standards are significant, I feel consumed by fear and related emotions, and to what end, I do not know.

I feel like very little progress has been made lately with this "recovery" process. Meanwhile, the rationale I've ascribed as the root cause gets further and further away and becomes less and less plausible. The thought this may never resolve or that what I am experiencing could be some form of early-onset dementia is terrifying. And yet, it feels more likely the longer this persists. I must consistently remind myself that what I have read points towards healing and restoration. Though for some, it takes longer.

All I know is that a couple of years ago, this wasn't part of my introspective self-dialogue. Now I find myself consumed by it because of the ever-present symptoms. They're subtle but stealthy. That's what makes this so hideous. A combination of emotional, psychological, and physical anomalies slowly picking at you. And, trying to take you down, like death by a thousand paper cuts.

I also applied to Starbucks several times. And aside from the occasional ding letter got no response, which I found odd because I would have been a formidable candidate for many of those positions. If ever there were an employer who knew the importance of blending art with design, given their warm and inviting aesthetic, it was certain to be Starbucks. I suppose it was just another example of how things can get overlooked in the bureaucracy of hiring, as well as the power of who you know, or who you don't, and timing. I've met several highly capable yet unspectacularly creative people over the years who have worked at Starbucks, some of whom I've mentored. I can't help but wonder how they broke the seal and got seen, let alone hired. One unifying factor among many of them? They had, at one time or another, worked at Microsoft.

About seven years ago, I was a candidate for a substantial creative role at Amazon. I was busy working full-time and didn't have a lot of time to take that *deep dive* into their whole interview paradigm, which is (come to learn) an essential prerequisite for getting any kind of serious look. (That would be "Principal 12," by the way, out of a set of fourteen that are foundational to their whole hiring process – learn these, and you're golden.) However, winging it as I did, I wasn't a complete schmuck. I did make it through to the final round.

A slight point of redemption: later that spring, I spotted the hiring manager sizing me up at one of my kid's soccer games. Where, I might add, my son was slicing it up on the field and destroying the competition. And as I like to fantasize, exorcising any perceptions of my own inadequacies along with it. (I'm so petty.)

The interview process with Amazon is intended to elicit responses that are succinct and measurable. And fit with their preconceptions of what they feel is the best answer. Fair enough. Successful candidates are graded heavily on the content of their responses. But I would argue disproportionately so, yielding personal interaction and experience to one's ability to memorize and recite thoroughly rehearsed soundbites. Seldom did they make eye contact during the interview. They were often looking down, busying themselves with frantic notetaking. As I was sitting there, I found myself wondering if I even wanted to be a part of such an impersonal culture – the whole experience was mechanical and strange. Why was I so eager to be a part of something that didn't want to be a part of me? I also discovered an interesting pattern across the leadership ranks – many were former Microsoft staffers.

June 15, Year Two

There have been moments recently when I've thought things were getting better, then suddenly I felt inept and went back to the starting line. It's the confusion and lack of mental focus that is scaring me. The prospect of taking on a new role seems as daunting as ever. I used to welcome these challenges. If I knew there was an end to this, a day when I'd wake up and feel relief, I think I could fake my way through, but the doubt is getting in the way. I may need to redefine my next chapter.

If healing is the outcome, I need more time. I must remind myself (through meditation and relaxation) that healing is indeed the inevitable outcome. Also, I cannot control what I cannot control, and my energy is best spent focusing on doing my best with what I have and not worrying too much about the future.

This is taking a toll on our marriage. I've had to check out inti-
mately this past year to hold myself together. I hope and pray that
my time on this earth hasn't peaked and that I am not on some
kind of rocky descent. I need a positive sign, a reminder of what it
means to feel healthy. To validate that I'm doing the right things
and stay the course. Feeling off-track day in and day out is simply
overwhelming. Please afford me the strength to let goodness flow
inward.

During any interview process, I've learned that words matter.
And having access to an assortment of responses to often painfully
broad questions is vital to convey preparedness and command of
the topics – and to stave off the dreaded mental blank. But I'm just
not that adept at conjuring up that script – it feels fake to me, especially as I get older. Not that I'm particularly jaded but the honest
answer, "Are you fucking kidding me, thousands of times ..." isn't
the best response to, "Have you ever experienced a conflict, and
how did you handle it?" The fact is, and isn't it enough? I've led and
completed countless projects, made clients millions of dollars, hired
dozens of people, let dozens go for a variety of reasons. Consulted
and confided with employees through personal crises, illnesses, and
bereavements; triumphed over failures; and succeeded mightily and
many times over, all with little fanfare. And, despite my tone, I'm
not a dick.

While interviewing with Amazon, I was considered for a
high-level position at Group Health Cooperative, which would
have put me in charge of a team of designers, writers, and content
producers. Upon wrapping up the interview process, the director
told me his decision literally came down to a coin toss – and not
to my advantage – bum luck. In hindsight, however, it was to my

advantage. A year and a half later, due to budget cuts, the role dissolved, as did the director's position. I would have been out on the street in less than eighteen months. The director would land on his feet just fine though. As sure as the sun sets in the west ... wait for it ... he had worked at Microsoft.

It was at about this time I realized I wasn't feeling right. My head felt fuzzy, and my thinking was becoming increasingly cloudy. I now know that my brain was affected by all the crap my doctor had prescribed. But I still hadn't made the correlation between the medicine and how I felt. By now, despite the concoction of sleep aids that my doctor recommended, I wasn't sleeping much. I was exhausted, which I attributed mostly to my recently diagnosed and unresolved sleep apnea. If I could go back, I would have sought a care provider who knew what the hell they were doing, who better understood the ramifications of administering and weaning off benzodiazepines. It was somewhat miraculous that I made it through these interviews as well as I did.

In the years that followed, I'd make it to second-round interviews with Mod Pizza (Starbucks/Microsoft leadership, just saying), Boeing, T-Mobile, and several other prominent local agencies but never quite got to the offer. As much as I didn't meet their expectations, I also found myself backing away, less sure of my capabilities, and distracted by a diminished sense of wellbeing and waning enthusiasm to take on a new role. Aside from how I was feeling physically, it occurred to me that I had little desire to be at any one of these places and had become more and more averse to making a change altogether.

I was attracted to the idea of being a part of something stable during an insecure and frightening period in my life, and these were scant attempts to remove myself from my current situation in search of a change of scenery. It was a running away of sorts. I was looking for an out, but I soon realized that it would take more than a new job to fix what had become progressively more difficult for me personally. Somewhere en route, I had gotten off track.

June 22, Year Two

Happy Father's Day. I was so enraged today. I feel so done. Camille's finished with me, and I've alienated the kids. All my prayers and hopes and this is where I end up? A leap in the wrong direction.

It's Monday, early morning, and a hard day awaits. What's next? Where do I go from here? Will there ever be peace? It's all I pray for. Not wealth. Not things. Simply peace and wellness. I pray for this every night. Right now, it feels so lonely and dark. Hopeless? Because it's been so long. I try to keep a positive head and yet find myself in the deepest well. I pray for a lift. I can only claw out so many times. Dear God, I pray for peace. Release me from this darkness.

No one understands the amount of pressure I'm under. Every day I must push myself to persevere. It's been like this for two years. I'm either certifiably nuts, or I've had to deal with something so excessively real that it's marginally beyond comprehension. I may never fully know.

A sense of blind ambition has followed me over the years and served me well in many respects. For me it was triumph through effort. I enjoyed the satisfaction of taking something on, the more challenging the better, and seeing it through to completion. A kind of performance complex I suppose but not meant to impress anyone, rather to prove to myself that I can achieve more than the average person, despite feeling somewhat inferior in other aspects of my life. I became super task-driven and was able to carve out a relatively successful path for myself. Not a bad formula, if a self-centered existence is what you're seeking.

July 6, Year Two

Last night was full of despair. Obsessive thoughts about work. I must remind myself not to read before bed – too much stimulation. I didn't meditate all weekend. Need to maintain my regimen.

I'm grateful for my current work status, but nothing was handed to me, no slack afforded. I've made it thus far on guts and toil, despite feeling less than 100% on point. When I started working at my current job, I intended to be there for maybe a year. It wasn't a place I saw myself long-term. However, it did afford me an exit from The Seattle Times, a bump in pay, and an opportunity to roll up my sleeves and once again exercise my creative side.

It was an unknown agency servicing a mishmash of retail clients spanning the mattress and automotive categories. A portfolio of work that I did not find particularly inspiring, but nevertheless, offered a variety of disciplines for me to grow into. I had carte blanche to run the creative department and was exposed to radio and TV production and video shoots for the first time. However, shortly after I started, I discovered it had this overly Christian vibe which made coming into the office awkward. There were Bibles placed strategically throughout the hallways and on coffee tables, and every Monday morning at 8:00, you had to make your way past the prayer session happening on the other side of the conference room glass doors. It was a bizarre way to kick off the week when all you really wanted to do was get to your desk and check your email. But I can think of worse activities, so I put up with it.

The owner has chosen to invest in several side businesses while also attempting to run the agency. However, the revenue to support those businesses has yet to materialize, putting the onus back onto the employees to do even more with ever diminishing resources. And consecutive years of declining revenue have borne this out. Ironically, he means well – maybe even to a fault. Trying to please colleagues, business partners, and clients at the expense of the prudent management of the enterprise.

But much more could be achieved by inspiring the staff and recognizing their contributions. Relationships are strengthened by listening and putting their needs first over the interminable misconception that the client reigns above all else. After all it's the employees that make things go. Manage expectations equitably, and successes will follow. Circumvent those efforts, and people's purpose, passion, and enthusiasm will wane, cratering morale and taking the business with it.

Fast forward fifteen years, and I am the sole remaining VP-level manager of several who came before me – three-deep at one point when the agency was once flush with cash. My areas of responsibility have only increased, as has the value I've added to the agency. Yet, I haven't had a raise in over seven years. I've considered leaving, but I'm on the cusp of aging out, making it more difficult to land those higher-level, lucrative positions. And, of course, my odds for landing one of those coveted roles would be that much more favorable if I had "you know what" on my resume.

It's not that I've put my current role at the center of my problems – I'm grateful for the sustained employment – this one's on me. But how did I end up in this situation? Intent to forge my own way, to set course and speed. And yet, here I am, affixed to another's ambition at the expense of my and other people's effort. I know there's a lesson here – I just can't put my finger on it. But my optimism suggests there are greener pastures ahead.

July 13, Year Two

My anxiety expresses itself through irrelevant obsessive thoughts in the late hours – it's like a switch comes on while I lie awake. I don't even remember what the thoughts are about. They just race through my head and circle around. They seem important at the time.

EIGHTEEN

ODE TO KYLE

Despite the infrequency of our paths crossing, it felt like we'd known each other much longer. We shared the kind of bond you have with someone you'd barely known and yet felt connected to at a much deeper level. To the extent that friends in common would remark, "Hey, you guys are so alike." "Yeah, I get that too," he might say back. An alliance expressed in subtle mannerisms as if in code, dialing into one another's minimalistic cues with precision. A grin, a nod – that's all it took, and we knew we were on the same page.

And there he lay that Sunday afternoon, flat on his back in the middle of the street, staring up into oblivion. Eyes glazed over, tears pooled up in the corners, looking outward, pupils tiny and lifeless – his life, yours in it, over in an instant. The bond severed yet resonant. The certainty of mortality, life's impermanence playing out in an instant. An actuality that this happened to him today as it will happen to all of us one day. Horrific, jarring, and transcendental, all at once. The unbearable pain this fathers' family will feel in just a few moments, indiscriminately, due to some weird stroke of fate that brought him to this place and time. Bad timing? Chance? Why today and why Kyle?

The knock at the door. The greeting of a cordial neighbor. "Sorry I disturbed you. I see you're reading a book." That's what flashed through my mind anyway because that's what I'd usually say – but there's no room for small talk now. The warm glow of the light, emanating from the living room. The backdraft of the evening air as it greeted these two worlds. An excruciating reality awaited, the last vestige of normalcy holding back a dam of emotion that is about to be uncorked. "I wonder what she's reading?" I couldn't help it. The pleasant aroma of artichokes nearing perfection. "Fuck, Chris, get on with it." He must have been looking forward to it because it was his night to cook – he had planned for it. He set the timer, and he was out of time. They all were. It was time.

I was the only one at the scene who knew him. It was up to me to get to his family as soon as possible. I was to be the messenger of the worst news possible, and who am I to handle this moment with the grace and dignity that it requires? My brain was already awash in confusion and distress – It isn't fair. Life isn't fair. I was qualified because I cared. "Kyle has been in a terrible accident," I unleashed as inevitability finally took hold.

Every time I cross that spot where he lay, I think of him. I wonder how and why his fate came to such an abrupt and senseless end. That any of us can be taken at any moment. I feel the resonant loss that emanates in our absence across the many lives we've touched, in ways that we will never fully realize. And because of this, and life's impermanence, and the casual interplay between chance and tragedy, the ridiculous calculation that this notion of "you and I" shouldn't be happening at all, we are once again left to contemplate life's purpose. To support each other in between these moments of finality, as if all of it mattered. Because we owe it to those who came before, who didn't have a chance to see out the clock and enjoy one last dinner with their family.

August 21, Year Two

Progress has been slow and only minutely perceptible. The mere duration of this supersedes the discomfort I initially felt. I would rather have had two broken legs, healed, and be done with it. The fact of not being fully restored after all this time makes me wonder whether I've lost a piece of myself. At what point does chronic be-come permanent? Do I keep believing that my thinking will become clearer someday, and I'll be able to sleep normally again without the tortuous thoughts? In many ways, it seems that I'm close to resolv-ing this – tantalizingly close, yet not fully there.

Kyle was one of the most experienced cyclists I knew. He was an exceptional rider and highly regarded by his peers within the racing community. Kyle had a few minutes to spare before his artichokes were ready and decided to take his bike out and test the adjustments he had made to his brakes. A minor, routine activity. So much so that he felt no need to change out of his flip-flops or put on a hel-met. He was just going around the block, something he had done hundreds of times, to return home within a few minutes. He could read the terrain through his palms and visualize every turn and un-dulation of the street. If it wasn't for traffic, he could have done the route blindfolded.

It was a beautiful summer evening, almost perfect, and I was in my driveway washing my camper. I was about a hundred feet up the hill from where the incident occurred – the view obstructed by a few hedges and a couple of trees. He would have ridden right past me. These brief encounters were often met with a dry "how's it going?" or a glance. But I didn't notice him this time around, with my head down, scrubbing the moss off the roof. Maybe I caught the buzz of his gears as he glided past, I'm not sure.

It couldn't have been more than five minutes after he slipped by when I became aware of the sirens. At which point I hurried down to see what was happening and, to my shock, saw Kyle, lying face-up on the pavement, with no discernible injury visible. He actually looked rather peaceful. He was being attended to by two medics who did what they could to stabilize him but didn't appear to be in any hurry, which I found odd. They must have known something by that look in his eyes. A few other neighbors were hovering nearby, concerned but unaware of who this stranger was lying in the middle of their street.

A couple minutes passed – he was unresponsive. I called out his name a few times but got no reaction. I then ran back up the hill to let Camille know what had happened; she was horrified. We immediately got in the car and sped to the other side of the block to inform his wife. At which point, Kyle had been transported to the hospital. I returned to the scene to learn more. There was talk and confusion amongst the police and others as to what could have happened. There was no clear answer, but I had my suspicions, and others were beginning to form theirs too.

The police investigators identified marks in the road that were caused by the bike hitting the asphalt, where the tumbling began. There was no indication that he had been struck by a vehicle. No debris, no skid marks, no evidence of an impact to his bike. He wasn't near an intersection. And we were all eyeing the unmarked asphalt bump in the middle of the road.

However, with no eyewitness to the actual incident, the immediate assessment was that this was a hit and run – that a car must have swerved out of its lane, clipped him, and taken off. Despite no screeching of tires, no revving engine, no auto-related fragments of any sort, this would be the official determination – the easy answer would satisfy the day. It didn't make any sense, but that's where they left things.

I was contacted by the press a few days after the accident. They were seeking information about what had happened. In my heart, I knew but was reluctant to share my perspective. I felt that recounting my point of view would only have upset the family, so I left it alone. A thorough investigation wasn't in the best interest of the city either. They must have known it. It would have been expensive to prove and defend, and any evidence would have been long gone by then. Speaking up was a judgment call, and I only had my gut to fall back on.

August 27, Year Two

I took a week off to get out of the office and rest despite not having any vacation plans.

I have this lump in my throat. The word "entrenched" comes to mind. An obsessive need to be by myself has crept in. It's uncomfortable. I hope that these anxious feelings associated with sleep resolve soon. With this cognitive state, I fear that something more long-term has set in.

My life has changed, and I don't know what's going to happen next. I'm not afraid of aging or necessarily dying, but a slow, drawn-out process would be unwelcome. For now, I'll keep focusing on the right things as best I can – pray, meditate, and hope.

What Really Happened

Kyle was testing his brakes that evening, and the hill in front of our house provided the perfect runway to work out the kinks. He knew what to expect because he'd taken this route many times before. But on this day, something was different. Unbeknownst to him, the terrain had been modified. It had been a few weeks since his last test run, and he was oblivious to the road obstacle that lay in wait. A critical section near the bottom of the hill, where he would have reached his peak gliding speed, had now been re-shaped into a virtually undetectable, unmarked, perfectly smooth hump spanning the road in the direction he would have been traveling. A berm rising three to four inches above the surface now loomed in wait.

Kyle was likely intending to coast to a top speed of around twenty-eight miles per hour by the time he reached that bottom section of the hill – fast enough to test the adjustments he'd made. He would have stayed to his left to avoid any vehicles that often parked off to the right, which on this day happened to be a van. And he would have steered clear of the raised manhole cover located in the center of the street between the parked van and the newly formed rise. The last thing on his mind would have been a speed bump in the middle of the road.

He wouldn't have seen it coming until he was on it – or even realized it was there until he was well out of his saddle. The only alternative "outs" would have been the manhole cover to his right, the ditch to his left, or simply to brace himself – none of which happened. He caught the best of the mound, which immediately ejected him from his pedals towards the front of the bike. At that speed, given the pitch, I suspect he and his bike went airborne for several yards before striking the pavement flip-flops first. An eternity to think of those artichokes in the oven, his family, those birthdays – sending him and his bike head-over-heels to their tragic resting place about sixty feet further down the hill.

Kyle was conscious and semi-alert for a few minutes. The first witnesses found him sitting up and dazed, progressively incoherent. He had probably just enough time to realize the tragic irony of his situation. "You've got to be kidding me?!" he must have muttered to himself. However, the hemorrhaging to his brain overtook him, and he lay back down and never regained consciousness.

A worker erroneously constructed a hazard in the middle of the road, and someone hastily signed off on the project – maybe they too were in a hurry to get home for their own dinners that night. Though far from their intent, these people contributed enormously to Kyle's death. An obstacle left unmarked for an unsuspecting cyclist to encounter. Commuters, protected by a steel undercarriage, bottoming out every time they passed over the hump, eventually got fed up, and within several weeks the city repaired the street.

They'd left a banana peel in the road, and they knew it. It would have been nice if they had stepped up and held themselves account-able for their role and made amends with the family, but to my knowledge, that never happened.

We will never fully realize how we affect other people's lives. I wonder how many peels I've left behind (fig. 34, p. 192).

September 7, Year Two

I went to sleep relatively easily last night. I drifted off within a reasonable amount of time but awoke abruptly from a weird dream. One of those lucid dreams that catch you between the unconscious and waking world.

I was startled by a vivid image of a face looking down at me, ob-serving me as I slept, only to be caught in the act as I awoke. It was just a head, no body, but not in a grotesque way. It was positioned just above me, looking down, not directly at me. More as if it were looking through me. Kind of pale, forlorn, almost gray in color, with long, flowing hair. I think it was a woman, but it was unrecogniz-able as anyone I knew. It wasn't a terrifying image, just disturbing. As I woke and looked up, the image began to fade. I was wide awake at this point and a bit freaked out, which left me feeling agitated for the rest of the night. I slept intermittently, drifting in and out. Strange.

NINETEEN

HAVING KIDS

I thought Camille and I were somehow inherently qualified to bring children into this world – that our diverse and well-rounded life experience made us impervious to the petty challenges that many parents face nowadays. And that it was our obligation to bestow upon our future offspring our hard-earned insights, which would invariably afford them certain advantages as they got older. And, in turn, instill a heightened sense of respect and gratitude towards those who raised them. I mean, come on, we *owed* it to the world to have kids.

But, fair to say, my delusions have since been brought down to earthly reality. I'm now happy to report that I realize how naive and self-absorbed that thinking actually was. My considerable wisdom today suggests that having kids is one of the most humbling experiences one could ever imagine because, as they often remind me, I'm pretty much stupid.

October 8, Year Two

On the one hand, I feel optimistic that I'm progressing towards normalcy. On the other, dark thoughts spiral me backward. One of the biggest impediments is not being able to relax into sleep. This should get better eventually, as I relearn to settle back into my normal rhythm and allow myself to drift off into a more natural state.

I recall the first few months, desperately trying to cling to my daily schedule. Checking the clock hour-by-hour, wondering how the hell I was going to make it through the workday, let alone the week. After several months of this, I settled into a no-man's-land head-zone. A foggy, hazy, third-person conductor, guiding my every action: wake, eat, work, meditate, exercise, sleep, rinse, repeat.

I've had a running injury to my Achilles for several months. More painful some days than others, it's been enough to slow me down and even sideline me on occasion. But I noticed the other day that the pain was not present during my run. For me, I think this is how the benzo-recovery process will play out. That there will be a time when I will reflect on my day and be comforted knowing that the unpleasant symptoms have simply up and left.

Our kids are amazing. We are blessed to have three who are healthy and relatively well-adjusted. But they drain the crap out of you. I like to believe, as the theory goes, exhaustion is validation for a job well done and that we've braved stepping into the ring for fifteen rounds and made it through the first ten relatively intact. Although our arms feel like lead, and we're exhausted, we keep taking the punches. Bring it.

Raising children is exhaustingly expensive. And not just from a financial standpoint – it's tough on the relationship. Sleep deprivation and a lack of time and energy rear their ugly heads in more ways than you can foresee. I understand why some parents check out. I do on occasion – for crying out loud, I'm writing a book! The temptation to abandon ship and get sucked into one's work can be oh so tantalizing. Raising children is a daunting commitment. It's a heavyweight sport.

November 9, Year Three

Suffice to say, I am disappointed not to be writing to celebrate my complete recovery from these symptoms. If you asked me two years ago if I'd still be living with the effects today, I would not have thought it possible. Its mere presence and persistence have added yet another layer of weight to the discomfort. I am grateful that I've made it this far and have sustained my subsistence, relationships, and work status. Though clouded in thinking and distracted often, I've managed to be a decent parent to my kids and have thus far weathered many of the real-life stressors that have piled up with relative success. But, for now, we stick with the plan. Hoping that a year from now, I can once and for all write that entry. "I made it; I feel well and can once again live the broader strokes of my life."

Sometimes I feel unqualified and even ill-suited to be a parent. Who am I charged with such a critical task, pretending to think that I know what I'm doing? And you know they can smell it, like blood in the water – It's a child's sixth sense (fig. 35, p. 192), endowed with an ability to reveal vulnerabilities that lurk within each of us parents, and to point them out at the most inopportune times. Camille and I play ping-pong with this sense of insecurity, often finding ourselves at our wits' ends, and yet thankful we have each other for support – to pull one another through the rough patches.

We finally decided to have kids in our mid-thirties – old enough to know better, as we like to joke. We had been enjoying each other's company and the lifestyle of having no attachments. Nevertheless, we got the itch to take our union to the next level. Although we had no burning desire to carpet-bomb our relationship with the responsibilities of bringing humans into this world, we felt ready enough and excited to make this next leap and face whatever adventure awaited us – and trash the carpet in the process.

However, a funny thing happened. Once the obligations completely took hold and the demands fully kicked in, at least for me, the days and months melded into years, then a decade passed, and before I realized it, fifteen years had gone by. And, lo and behold, our children had grown into young adults. Wait ... what?

I'd heard about this kind of thing happening to others, but nevertheless, I felt short-changed. I seemed to have missed out on something, maybe even everything. I was there, but was I there enough? Did we do enough? I know we weren't perfect, but did we get it right, and does it even matter? The bittersweet reckoning for me in all this is that I wish I had done more or allowed more of myself to be present when I was there, to appreciate the little moments when they were younger. To take it all in, slow things down a bit and let it unfold more organically, shoot from the hip more often. But let's face it, these lessons don't really jive with our culture, let alone with the expectations we place on ourselves to adequately provide for our families – the concept of the American dream isn't exactly tied to reality. To dream, by definition, is to take us out of the here and now.

December 2, Year Three

The problems I'm currently experiencing are the accumulation of real-life stressful circumstances compounded by the lingering effects of my medication. This creates an overly active cycle of stress, inhibiting my ability to regulate these processes more naturally. In essence, feeding on itself. I believe the PTSD reaction I'm experiencing is stress-induced in anticipation of this cycle and the symptoms that I experience, to varying degrees each day.

[If a doctor left an implement in your body after surgery, they'd be held accountable. But not so much if they exposed you to a brain-altering drug and something happened. There is virtually no recourse after this sort of "invisible" injury has occurred. That kind of "leave-behind" is more difficult to prove. I read the other day that about 13 percent of the U.S. population is taking some form of a doctor-prescribed benzodiazepine. While an additional 13 percent is taking antidepressants of some sort – and the long-term effects of either, are still not fully known. We're on our own when things don't go as planned. I wasn't motivated to pursue legal action – I just wanted to test the waters and see if anyone gave a shit.]

[Be forewarned. This is the part where I talk about my kids, so go easy with the eye rolling pal.]

Ruby

I couldn't have imagined that one day I would have two sons and a daughter. It really wasn't something we planned. We just kind of rolled with it. We openly welcomed what the universe had to offer, and we were so fortunate. And yet I still wonder, "How DID this happen?" Just yesterday, we were unattached, living freely, and now we face all the responsibilities that come with parenting three distinctly different human beings!

Ruby is naturally beautiful with delicate features, slender, and on the tall side. She's funny and witty. And enjoys dressing up and hanging out with her friends. She's also a gifted athlete committed to reaching the top of her sport, a creative thinker, a connoisseur of art, and someone who aspires to make the world a better place. We work hard to ensure the soccer obsession doesn't become too overwhelming, encouraging her other interests. To stay grounded, she enjoys painting, sewing, or binge-streaming re-runs of my old schoolmate Dwight. And she can be a teenager too, as she signals for more personal space, sometimes in not-so-subtle ways.

Ruby is a typical fifteen-year-old in many respects. Perfecting her nails, keeping up with the correct ratio of ear piercings, wearing marginally appropriate clothing. One of the mixed blessings that go along with being her parent has been watching her form her own identity. Less reliant on Mom or Dad to make the world right when things aren't going so well, opting to spend time alone in her room, immersing herself in social media. What once could be fixed with a hug, or a well-timed scoop of ice cream is now more elusive and out of our hands.

She'll have an opportunity to go to the best schools one day because she'll have worked her way there. She already displays the makings of a leader because of her capacity to form relationships with just about anyone. And it wouldn't surprise me to see her rise to success, recognized by her peers for her authenticity, dedication to her chosen craft, and empathetic heart. But, in my eyes, no matter which path she chooses, Ruby's already achieved more as a person than I could ever have imagined – all our kids have. I just hope she'll continue to find joy in her journey as her story unfolds.

Ruby attracts positive things. Over the past couple of years, she's been the subject of a video documentary tracking young female soccer players as they aspire to play the game at the highest level. It's too soon to tell how far this would go. Nevertheless, it's been an exciting project for her to be a part of. The documentary culminated in a trip with her mom to the Women's World Cup tournament in Lyon, France the summer of 2019, where she formed friendships with people from different parts of the world she would otherwise never have met.

Lughano was attending boarding school in Connecticut as a scholarship-sponsored athlete from Malawi and had planned to spend a couple weeks with us over spring break. Ruby hadn't seen her since they first met in Lyon earlier that summer and was excited to introduce Lughano to her friends, show her around school, and train with her on the team. About a week after she arrived, Covid-19 overwhelmed the country (the world for that matter), and everything began to shut down, including air travel and schools. Her short visit had now become an open-ended stay.

The girls made the most of their time together, regularly training hard and pushing each other to be better athletes (fig. 36, p. xx). Weeks turned into months, at which point Lughano officially became a part of the family. Their relationship had evolved into mutual respect as collaborators, working towards a common goal, as well as laying the seeds for an enduring friendship. It would be six months before Lughano finally returned to the east coast to resume her in-person schooling and another two months before she went home to see her mother, sister, and extended family.

Lughano is a terrific kid, mild-mannered and wise beyond her years. It was a blessing to have her in our home and share in many of her new and exciting experiences, such as learning to swim, wading in the Pacific Ocean for the first time, playing card games, and roasting marshmallows around the campfire. We look forward to watching her journey unfold as well and spending even more time together in the not-so-distant future.

Note to Ruby while she was struggling with mounting challenges brought on by the pandemic.

Just want to let you know how proud I am to be your dad. I can't imagine how difficult these past several months have been for you – the stay-at-home demands, sharing your space with Lughano for such a long time, and managing all those college inquiries and uncertainties. I know it's not been easy. But just know, even during those more difficult days, you are the center of our universe, and we'll always be here for you. Keep up the hard work and be sure to make time for yourself!

Ruby's going to be OK because she has no desire to be anything other than herself. Recently, I've learned to keep my expectations in check, to clear the way for whoever it is she is to become. To want anything other than for her to be happy would be an imposition on our relationship. She and her siblings have already accomplished amazing things and are becoming productive and conscientious young adults. And to "expect" anything beyond that would be un-realistic and self-serving. At this stage, it's fun to simply be an ob-server, the benefactor of her dreams, and to see what happens next.

May 30, Year Three

I can feel the familiar night-time wave of irrational anxiety come over me as I lie awake. It's not as bothersome as in the past, but still irritating. The fears are irrational. Having just read an ar-ticle of little consequence, my thoughts contain images and snippets wrapped in meaningless scenarios, running, looping, spinning in my mind. A familiar sense of fear and dread in anticipation of the upcoming week looms, and yet there's nothing out there to cause alarm or concern. My psyche is run amok in what otherwise should be my quiet time. Random bursts of stress-like energy bounce off the neurological walls of my private asylum.

As a parent, I'm learning to challenge myself, to recognize when it's appropriate to step back and relinquish control – in other words, to get the hell out of the way! Giving our children latitude may be difficult, but it's necessary to help them learn to become indepen-dent. Naturally, we want to fix, protect, and hold close. And yet, letting go is the inevitable outcome. And one of the hardest things a parent will have to face.

Many parents invest so much time planning out their kid's lives: what they should wear, where to attend school, what team to be on, that parents come to believe the path they have set is the per-fect option. So much so that they risk missing out on what matters most – their child's well-being. It's a strange dichotomy – so much forethought and scheduling and yet affording them little say in the matter.

If we allow our children to practice who they are early and often, we help them develop confidence and become self-reliant. Rather than hold steadfast to a singular path or criticize them for not meeting expectations, we must seize the opportunity to recalibrate and discover what it is they do excel at – even if it shakes things up. We need to let go of preconceptions and accept their unique gifts.

To correct them for drawing outside the lines, question why they missed that goal, or focus on that one B rather than the other five A's, chips away at their self-esteem and only adds stress to the family dynamic. I recall numerous instances of having to hold my tongue. Wondering why David couldn't connect on that perfect pitch, feeling a sense of frustration when Liam was overtaken by a runner, or letting one slip altogether, when, try as she might, Ruby missed a blocked shot.

By trading in our disappointed reactions for opportunities for encouragement, we can provide fertile ground for our children to explore and discover their essence. It's necessary to exercise awareness and recognize when it's appropriate to step aside and allow them to relish in their successes, clean up their messes, and develop the tools they'll need to dust themselves off when they do fail.

July 27, Year Three

I recall thinking to myself there would be no way that I could sustain this for much longer. Let alone for weeks and months, and yet here we are. At first, they were tiny weights in my hands, but they became increasingly heavier over time, eventually almost pulling my arms out of their sockets. Today it's once again tolerable yet ever-present. This tells me that the symptoms have subsided and/or that I've strengthened my resolve.

I've been experiencing weird, drunken dizziness upon waking, which I've never felt before. My eyes track to the right when trying to focus on an object. Kind of like the spinning sensation after having had too much to drink. I'm not taking any medication to cause this, and the only supplements I'm ingesting are the Cal/Mag blend and 1 mg of melatonin at bedtime.

Haven't had that lucid "window" that many speak of, at least not within the past eighteen to twenty-two months. Until then, all I can do is continue to think positively and do what is healthy for my mind and body. Still looking for "closure."

David

Tall, with fluffy blond hair and a slight build, people often get me and David confused from afar. He has well-proportioned, chiseled features, which are distinct and well-defined. In the summer, his tanned face accentuates the creamy-white peak atop his head as well as the big blue eyes he got from his mom. He has my gentle demeanor, though he is more empathetically aware than either one of us was at his age. He has a goofy sense of humor and is somewhat shy around people he doesn't know very well.

Whatever our shortcomings as parents, David appreciates what we have as a family. And that our time together won't last forever. David is averse to hurry things along. That's how I like to think of it anyway. He isn't lazy ... he is loving. He doesn't express his affection in words so much, but in how he reacts to certain situations – a reassuring smile or expression of gratitude. And a preference to hang out with his parents on a Friday night. He feels reassured knowing his family is nearby.

He struggles at times with his emotions, racking up bills for broken video-game controllers and cell phones hurled in frustration, followed by swear volleys lofted mostly at himself. But these episodes pass quickly. And he is the first to catch himself, to admit his momentary lapses, offer an apology, and make good on any mishaps that may have resulted from his actions.

As a kid, I didn't take the time to think beyond my immediate needs and wants – but David sees the struggles we face as parents and acknowledges the sacrifices we've made to keep him in sports, plan for his future, and ensure his needs met. He's observed pushback from his siblings and has chosen to bypass much of the drama. He has his moments too, but from what I can tell, he is much further along than many his age, and quite a few my own.

As a younger boy, David sensed the impermanence of life and mourned the passing of his own childhood. Rather than coast into that next chapter, as many of us do, he was reflective of his early years. He missed being a little kid. There was a time when watching home videos was too painful. He would get emotional watching his younger self play with his Hot Wheels, kicking the ball around, his "Binky" corked tightly in his mouth. We all lament from time to time, but he seemed to recognize how fleeting life can be, the feelings associated with letting go, and that change is inevitable but not always welcome. Most of us do not experience this level of self-awareness until we are faced with some type of trial later in life. And yet, here he was, at the age of twelve, taking notice, thinking introspectively, fully aware that he was in the process of transitioning into a different person.

All three went to the same primary schools and followed their mom's mandate to pursue music. Under the direction of Mr. E, Eckstein Middle School had an exceptional jazz program. They would compete in music competitions around the country and often score highly, if not win it all! Liam excelled at trombone and guitar, and Ruby in vocal jazz. David showed an interest in the trombone too, and Mr. E was astute enough to point out that he had a "gift" and that practicing "would go a long way." But David had neither the patience nor the motivation to take it much beyond the classroom. Camille and I recognized his ability to recall melodies and vocalize complex solos note-for-note, as well as his refined sense of timing and musical nuance. But that he displayed an unwillingness to put in the work to learn the full range of an instrument. For Mom and Dad, it was another exercise in letting go.

I think there comes a time when opportunity aligns with the gifts that lie dormant within each of us. But many of us are too distracted living out our practical lives and miss out on these callings. However, through messing around with sound-mixing software, David discovered a medium that would finally allow him to express his musical talent. It became clear that he wasn't interested in any one instrument but that he loved the idea of stitching instruments together to form sounds that he could relate to. Which led to his passion for creating "beats," a genre of hip-hop that has enabled him to produce, publish, and sell his own creations online to aspiring singers and songwriters throughout the world. He is currently building an audience that may one day provide him with a sustainable, if not substantial income. For all my entrepreneurial longing, the next best thing is to see your kids find a way to make something work for themselves. Or maybe it is the best-best thing.

Like his siblings, David is a gifted athlete but prefers moderation and focus over dabbling in all things. He likes to participate in many activities, but aside from soccer and maybe basketball (tetherball and four-square in his early career), he tends to steer clear of the uber-competitive fervor so often found in sports. David enjoys music, skiing, poker, and video games. But it is the social aspect with friends that reigns over that chase for adrenaline.

As a soccer player, David has the touch of a Kung Fu Panda. He approaches the game as a form of self-expression, an exercise in precision and refinement, and finds immeasurable joy when all the pieces come together in perfect harmony. He can deliver the ball at a full sprint, on a crowded pitch, in "traffic," as they say, accurately to a teammate rushing the goal. And it is this skill that will enable him to continue to play at the elite level at Saint Martin's University in the fall as a freshman, a competitive NCAA Division II program. At 6'4", light, and nimble, he's one of the most effective attacking center-midfielders in any league (fig. 37, p. 192).

David is like an old dog in the best sense of the expression, content to share your space, curl up at your feet, and emanate warmth and unconditional love. Like an old dog, David is accepting and forgiving. And quick to reward with kindness. I already told him not to bother with goodbyes when he heads off to college. Because it will be too difficult for me when the time comes – but he already knew that. Camille and I relish the thought of all the goodness that David will bring to this world. And to the fortunate few who will have the privilege of having him in their lives.

November 14, Year Four

If the definition of "permanent" means having a condition for at least a few years, then I think this would qualify. The body and spirit have a way of not wanting that to be so. Therefore, we continue the fight. This presents a kind of paradox. If this is indeed permanent, then what other treatments should I pursue to try and alleviate the symptoms? If it's still tied to the withdrawal of the medication, then other treatments may slow the healing process. What to do? The other symptoms I'm dealing with right now are generalized anxiety, sleep disruption, ringing in the ears, cognitive confusion, and fragmented memory. I yearn, hope, and pray that the healing will continue. I want to be one of those people who can say this happened to them, and it made them stronger.

Kids just want to be heard and understood. But it can be difficult for them to express what it is they want – because they often don't know. As a parent, I've found myself having to do this dance to try and get information out of them, only to be told, in no uncertain terms, to mind my own business. But we persist. Seemingly futile attempts to try and make a connection – direct questions, passive conversations, whatever it takes to crack the seam and find a way in.

Kids have the best poker faces when they want to, and you can never quite tell what's happening on the other end or whether what you're saying is affecting them or not. They do sometimes reveal hints of hope, in the form of an empty dishwasher without being asked, enough to suggest that they are listening. Little clues, re-assuring moments that things will be OK – that we got some of it right. These nuggets of goodness can be fleeting though but rewarding when noticed.

Raising kids is about expecting little in return. But who doesn't want to hear "thank you" more often? The more we expect of them, the more likely it is that we'll be disappointed. If we become disappointed, we tend to express it in the form of criticism, which only erodes their self-worth and pushes them away over time. We don't mean to do this. It just happens. Because we're "stupid." Can we really be disappointed when they didn't drive that runner home, got a B on that test despite trying, came in third instead of first …? We can disagree on many things. But disappointment must be reserved for those big-ticket items because disappointment changes the relationship.

But we will be disappointed with our children one day – it's inevitable: we're only human. And unfortunately, it will most likely be for the wrong reasons – because the vision we have for them has been challenged. We must be thoughtful in our reactions and have faith in what may seem like a counterintuitive process – letting go.

Letting go of how we think things ought to be and accepting how they are, as they play out in real-time, in ways only our children can express. We must make this part of our daily practice – to fortify their being rather than diminish it, so they develop into well-adjusted adults, and we can evolve into the caring stewards that are so essential to their lives.

The validation and respect we seek will one day find its way home in unexpected ways, like a subtle thank you expressed in a rinsed dish. That's the hope anyway.

February 18, Year Four

Tomorrow is going to be a great day. Healing is happening now and will continue throughout the night. Attitude is important. A positive outlook even in challenging times is possible. Live in the now. Be grateful for all the things in my life: kids, family, house, job, friends, and overall health. Today was a good day – tomorrow is another great adventure. Heal now.

Liam

A stubborn old soul, Liam was ready from day one to take on the world. With a tuft of red hair and sharp blue eyes, he was alert the moment he was born. Something about him said "little man" right away, and thus, we felt aptly named. His attentiveness, coordination, his whole demeanor put him well ahead of the curve. Moments after he arrived, he scanned the room inquisitively while the doctor made the two-yard handoff over to the exam table. Liam made eye contact with the staff as they cleared his airway and checked his vitals. Rather than cry, he had this look of consternation as if to say, "enough already, let's get on with it!" And if he could, he would have skipped over all that early development fuss and dove headlong into the rest of his life (fig. 38, p. 192).

Liam virtually bypassed that whole learning-to-walk phase. He went from his knees to the hundred-yard dash in one fell swoop. Liam enjoys doing and trying many different things. Camille saw this early and got him involved in as many activities as possible. Otherwise, it was all but certain ... trouble would find him. Baseball, basketball, soccer, track, Legos, airsoft, chess, games, cards, skiing, guitar, art, skateboarding, longboarding, cross-country, hacky sack, wrestling, flag football, swimming, taking stuff apart, and trying to put it back together: all were enthusiastically embraced by our busy-minded, active kid. He loved the variety and was seldom content doing just any one thing, yet he always remained hyper-focused.

Despite iron deficiencies and chronic respiratory irritants, he was a three-time top-three State finalist on his high school 3A 400-meter relay track team – earning an all-time school record with the team his senior year. At fifty seconds flat for the quarter mile, and a sub-two-minute half, Liam could move (fig. 39, p. 192). But despite these inherent gifts and interests, there's a solemnness to his non-conforming ways. He can be melancholy at times, determined to find his own way and avoid revealing too much of himself in the process.

One day we received an anonymous letter from a parent of one of Liam's friends, concerned about all the dare-devilish things he'd been involved with. Activities that we'd been aware of and highly discouraged but nevertheless began to take on greater visibility the further out he ventured – climbing bridges and buildings, teasing fate at harrowing heights. Escapades that he artfully documented on video and posted to the internet. But somewhere in there, he had enough sense to not stick his neck out too far. Or maybe he just got lucky. The more we reasoned, the harder he'd push back. His capacity to see how his behaviors affected others was obscured, shielded by an impenetrable layer of pride. More intent to pursue his ambition rather than allowing compassion to shape his decisions.

Because he is so headstrong and capable, Liam is not the kind of kid who takes well to ultimatums. The approach would only incentivize him and be used as fuel to cut out on his own – to follow through with the clues he'd dropped years earlier in that delivery room – to get on with the show! In my view, I didn't see this as a viable approach – a hill worth dying on. Having had faith that the longer we kept him engaged, the better the chances that our intent would eventually get through – that it was in our best interest to take the punches and reaffirm the power his actions have over others. Our role as parents evolved to proprietor of his wellbeing. We let him know we cared through encouragement and held steadfast to our values. And communicated regularly, revealing the path forward as best we knew how. Letting go of our preconceptions was the right course of action, even if it was gut-wrenching at times.

Excerpt from a note I wrote to Liam during the summer between his Sophomore and Junior years in college.

When things aren't going right, sometimes it feels the best way around is to skirt the issue. To not accept things for what they are and craft a narrative that suits our interests. But this is an illusion. I get it – I'm guilty. I've said and done things to avoid facing the consequences. But I can tell you, habits formed early and often are difficult to undo. Incidences avoided by not telling the truth have a way of catching up with us.

Liam's pretty much fully baked, as far as our work is concerned. We still pay most of the bills, and he has a couple of years left in school. But at twenty, the dynamics are much more about reason and support than telling him what to do. Our effort to give him space is proving effective. He's come to see that we are his allies, rather than viewing our input as an imposition to living out his true nature. I think he's finally come around to trusting our motives, which has helped strengthen the relationship and lay groundwork for a brighter future.

February 27, Year Four

A significant "win" for me over the past month has been tolerating sleeping with Camille. It's taken over three years – sad but true. Hard to believe. Hopefully, this is just another step towards restoration. In what I've been experiencing symptomatically and the toll it's had on the relationship. This is huge.

In my assessment, one of three things is happening. My brain is slowly degrading, which is a depressing thought – but which honestly seems more likely given each passing day, week, month, and year. I'm stuck with a pharmaceutically induced brain injury for the rest of my life. Or, though injured, still in a healing-flux pattern that has yet to resolve. The latter is what's supposed to happen if you read the feedback from others who've had a similar experience. At this point, you want to know.

Have I given up on the fact that this may never fully go away? Getting close. I'm kind of in a weird headspace given that so much time has elapsed, plagued with the sinking feeling that something still isn't quite right. I'm healed, when THAT feeling goes away. I would think that for a healthcare professional making pharmaceutical recommendations on behalf of patients, this would be one of those "good to know" things. "Here's something to help you relax, but oh ... by the way, it could really fuck you up – have a nice day."

We say we want our children to become independent, but let's face it, somewhere in there, we also want something for ourselves: an outcome we can say we're proud of – an accomplishment we can step back from and marvel at our handiwork. And I'll be damned, kiddo, if you threaten that vision! Children can usually smell this "refinement" a mile away. I'm not saying our aspirations for them are not coming from a well-intentioned place, but some kids are more driven to be free of these influences than others, if not downright rebellious. And it can sometimes be difficult to step aside and let them be who they need to be.

October 12, Year Four

As I venture ever closer to the end of what's called the "protracted symptomatic timeline," there are many wins worth celebrating. I remember that early on I didn't care if what I was experiencing lasted a month, a year, or longer. But it was the "not knowing" that proved to be most challenging. It was that feeling of open-endedness, wondering whether you're going to make it through the week, let along through the day, that was cause for great distress. But I take solace in knowing that progress has been made.

As our children get older, as they interact more and more with the world, we must remind ourselves they are travelers in a foreign land. Explorers seeking refuge in unfamiliar places, developing new friendships and interests, not fully aware of who they are or where they're headed. They are vulnerable and curious souls, unable to fully speak the language, unsure of the native customs, with only rudimentary survival skills. These are their testing grounds. Did we equip them sufficiently that they may thrive? Once again, the training wheels come off, but this time when they topple, the hope is that they have the skills to right themselves and keep on going.

It can be heartbreaking to sit idle as your kids confront these real-world responsibilities. Especially in the beginning, when all you can do is observe as they muddle their way along. And as much as you want to be the hero, to try and fix things as you've done so many times before, you now find yourself helpless. Relinquishing your role as "protector" to that of "listener" (if you're even fortunate enough to have been afforded that level of proximal duty). To watch and see if what you've taught them over the years will be enough to get them through.

When they're younger, we intuitively step into the role of raising and actively shaping their little lives. But these responsibilities are short-lived. In fact, independence is the endgame. Even from the beginning, separation is inevitable. You have them, so you can un-have them – that is the purpose. Having a mindset of preparing them for the "un-having" doesn't mean abandonment – the opposite, in fact – it means cultivating a loving, respectful environment in which they can evolve into who they are to become. And exercise those opportunities early and often.

November 22, Year Five

Last night I looked down at my hand, sensing something was missing and realized my wedding ring was gone. Not a big deal, typically, but this was my third ring, maybe fourth – I can't quite remember. Usually, a moment of recall would stir to light that I'd left it next to the bed, on the nightstand, by the bathroom sink, whatever. Nope, just gone. Not too alarmed, just frustrated. Another reminder of the past few months, pocked with poor memory, an inability to focus or

think clearly, marked by the constant drip of adrenaline filtering
through my body, 24/7.

So, why did we choose to have children and subject ourselves to such a life-altering experience and the sacrifices that go along with it? For me, it wasn't so much about having a well-thought-out plan as it was about following the natural order of things. That we felt in our hearts, it was simply our time. Was this irresponsible? Having a "playbook" would have been nice. And I do envy the notion of having been more financially stable. But I also can't help but wonder whether it would have been even more irresponsible had we followed our heads and opted out altogether. I mean, are we ever fully ready? How different our lives and how poorer the world would have been (aha, I was right!) if we had decided not to have kids simply because we didn't feel fully prepared.

I have this sinking feeling knowing that one day the party will end. That, having raised the tadpoles, we must face life's ultimate reconciliation and release them into the wild. As parents, we all know it's coming but tend to ignore it until the day finally meets us head-on. It's the inevitable conclusion: our time has passed. But what is the point of investing our guts into their lives if only to have them up and leave? Most people I know just kind of roll with this outcome – or keep it to themselves. But for me, it only amplifies the importance of bringing children into this world in the first place. That one day, they will cast off to make their own decisions, seeding the way for future generations. So yeah, if mistakes were made, they can blame Mom and Dad.

The sooner we do not make it about ourselves, the better. And the better off our children will be. I wish we could all enter the early phase of raising children understanding this. To make it our mission to seize those little moments more often, take pause, and take it all in. To key into the clues and insights, they reveal as they begin to walk and talk and interact with the world and not discount them as falling outside of the plan because they ARE the plan. There are countless opportunities to fan their tiny sparks of unique goodness. We have to let them know they are important and worthwhile, regardless of our preconceptions. Refrain from reactions of disappointment, of any sense that they're not measuring up, and construct each interaction with love and acceptance, strengthening their confidence so they may become healthy human beings. It's a lofty endeavor, but the dividends are great.

Take away the expectations and nurture their gifts, whatever those might be – not what you would like them to be. Provide the guardrails but not the road map. Because these traits, fanned early, not discarded or constrained to some preconceived notion, would mean a planet full of confident, creative, loving, and accepting humans. All you've got to do is look around to understand we're not there yet. As a community, as a society, as a culture, as a planet – there's room for improvement.

If I could trade one thing for the pain of letting them go, it would be for some kind of assurance that we've instilled within them a desire to help others. Letting go takes a leap of faith. And as you begin to remove the bumpers, as their teenage years unfold, you can't help but wonder whether you did enough. As it is, we can only look back and hope we didn't mess things up too bad. No plan, no playbook. We just ran with it. Time will tell.

November 28, Year Five

We all live in the clouds. Some more than others. Vaguely aware of their edges, size, and circumference. Opaque and impermeable. At times, fully enveloped, unable to recognize the presence of the outside world. And yet ever-changing, like a body of clay succumbing to the touch of invisible hands. A goat standing, leaning, and contorting – separating itself from the herd. Alone, wandering and wondering, seldom content to just be.

TWENTY

Mom

It was early May of 2012, and Camille and I were sitting in the lobby at Canadian customs, waiting to board our ship, when I got the text.

A few days earlier, I met up with Scott and Kent at my parent's home in Port Ludlow. Mom was in hospice care by now, resting in relative comfort, with the cats taking shifts at her feet. I remember the stillness of the room and the soft light coming through the windows casting amorphic shapes onto the walls. It felt serene, almost otherworldly as if the stage was being set for a grand entry – or exit. It reminded me of the endless space and energy I had experienced years earlier those two nights while Stephen lay in the hospital.

As the days wore on, Mom would drift in and out. But she was mostly with us. The grandkids raised her spirits when they were around. They spoke of light things. Liam knew what was happening more than Ruby and David, but the gravity of the moment was still beyond his reach. Once they said their goodbyes, I decided to stay behind an extra day while Camille headed home early with the kids to get them back to school and settled in with the sitter – to prepare for our overnight repositioning cruise from Vancouver.

Over those remaining few days with mom, I would check in often. But the bedside visits made her sad. Reminders that she knew her time with us was limited. Between vigils, my brothers and I reminisced, watched TV, and ate frozen leftovers – remnants of meals she had prepared months earlier for dad. Mom always made the best dinners.

Dad had waited too long to call in the full-time care, which only added to the strain. He was committed to seeing this through as best he knew how. Gary wanted to remain by Patti's side for as long as possible and attend to her needs. To be with the person who stuck with him throughout all those years, whatever it took. He was tired too and wasn't thinking clearly. If he could, he would have taken her place.

Despite her fading state, mom didn't want her time with us to end. Not now, not in that way – her partner having to tend to her most personal needs. She wanted our memories of her to be as she was. But nothing could have diminished the dignity of someone who lived life so selflessly, lovingly, and with such vitality. Who dedicated her life to bringing joy to others.

There is comfort in knowing that someone you love is nearby and present. There is guilt, too, having to concede that it is time to move on and bear witness to the ultimate passage, despite the longing for them to remain present for as long as possible. It is where these crossroads meet that we face life's greatest challenge. To let go and to be left behind reveals who we are.

Mom fought to the end, never resigned to moving on. That spirit is why she survived twenty-five years after she was first diagnosed with breast cancer. She wanted to live. She was a fighter. The thought of leaving her children was unbearable. She wanted more time to see her grandkids grow and enjoy a few more Christmases with her family. It was her hope to make it to eighty-five, but here she was at seventy-two, being taken by circumstances beyond her control – the almighty referee stepping in to call the match. I am grateful for the years we shared, the joy she brought us, and the love and light she shone upon our lives.

It was everything I could do to comfort her as I held her hand for the last time. To reassure her that everything would be OK. And thank her for being my mom. I would wait until she drifted off. This was the best time because she was at peace. Then I gently tucked her hand under the covers and walked out of the room. I let go. Leaving her that spring morning was the hardest thing I have ever done.

And there we were, sitting in customs. Reading the text, wishing I was with her. Mom had passed. But she knew she was loved, and I knew I was as well, and that is all that mattered. I wish I was by her side in her final moments. To be with her as she drifted away, as she had been there for me countless times when I needed her.

When they are no longer around, only then do you fully realize the remarkable effect people have on you. She made the little things special, whatever they were, and nothing escaped her attention. Mom lived her purpose – she was kind. If I can be half the person she was, I know I will have added value to this world.

December 27, Year Five

Christmas weekend coalesced into a restless night. Family issues, worrying about the kids, and a lot of fear around my mental state. It's hard to say whether I feel worse. Although Monday morning, I felt sad, fearful, and frustrated. Given where I'm at, four years into this process, it's depressing still to be experiencing this level of discomfort. I want to remain hopeful. But I am learning to cope with a permanent disability. In my efforts to get back to feeling "normal" I've reduced my meditation time – maybe this has had an effect. I also just stopped drinking coffee in the morning. Perhaps that's messing with things as well. Once again, the mantra is wellness and healing.

I believe the anxiety that wakes me three or four times every night is somehow amplified by whatever happened to me four years ago. Even the issues I was having then do not compare to what I'm experiencing now. I awake with a feeling of worry. Usually, I fall back to sleep within a reasonable amount of time. Periodically, during high-stress periods, I remain awake in a blurry, fearful state of semi-consciousness. It feels like I'm losing it at times. I'd say most people experience episodes like this occasionally, but it has been consistent for me for several years.

I've been experiencing zombie-like exhaustion lately. My cognitive function and memory slow as a result. It takes a more effort and deliberate focus to stay in tune with basic tasks. There's this weight pushing against the back of my eyes, filling up my middle-head like a giant cotton ball.

At this point, my goal is to make it through the year then explore alternative approaches towards wellness. Check off any potential degenerative brain ailments or other diseases and blood-borne illnesses or deficiencies. If it's depression that I'm fighting, I will look at carefully testing medications that may bring relief.

TWENTY-ONE

COMMON SENSE

I think the notion of common sense as a social binder has shifted off its axis. It's become the go-to reference for antagonists to express superiority over others: "My view matters most because you clearly 'lack' common sense." To me, this clever approach only underscores people's unwillingness to change or be wrong and their inability to truly listen to what others have to say. It's unkind. It's like we're stuck in a self-protective mode, reluctant to let our guard down and accept other people's points of view. Since when did any group corner the market on being "right?"

I was listening to a radio talk show the other day in which I found the term "common sense" (or lack thereof) tossed around so much I felt I must somehow be a part of the consociation. But, with every point the host made, its power was negated with a divisive comment – a quip at the expense of a larger group – indeed the majority. It's such a waste when someone with the means, intellect, and capacity to reach so many squander the opportunity to make real change, settling for a neutral effect at best. Intent to perpetuate an antagonistic point of view with an otherwise captive audience, who would benefit mightily from a message of hope over disruptive rhetoric.

I use the term "common sense" not as a tool to disparage and divide but rather to describe what is truly common amongst everyone in our quest to create harmony over disruption. So that it may benefit the populace and not just a narrow or divisive agenda – to unite and bring people together rather than accentuate our flaws. A declaration of kindness.

Maybe we just need a new phrase for "common sense." Or at the very least, to rethink how we've adapted it to describe the behaviors of others whom we simply do not agree with – the term was never meant to be an axiom for, "you're an idiot if you don't believe what I believe." I mean, that's only common sense.

If we do not grow up within a kind and supportive environment, we become hurtful and defensive, and less prone to the openness others have to offer. And, when we adopt this outlook (as many of us do to some degree), we're likely to take offense when confronted with differing points of view, especially when we perceive them to be a threat to our way of life. We close ourselves up due to the many letdowns, insults, and missed expectations dished out by our well-intentioned caregivers – parents, teachers, and the community. And this accumulation of weighty baggage hardens our sensibilities over time.

Consequently, we learn to latch on to the things or ideas that make us feel better, to fill a void of sorts (a talk-show host who's driven by the need to lash out at those who don't see things his way). We become an overbearing parent or a bully, or, more subtly, we adopt an indifferent or unsympathetic view of the world. It's only natural. I'm teased, I hurt, I hate. In essence, to make up for the lack of kindness shown to us when we needed it most, as impressionable young people in the many different contexts meaningful to each of us at the time. Who am I to say that telling a child not to act a certain way isn't crushing to their young, developing psyche?

When those closest to us let us down, we cling to the beliefs that lessen the pain – food, objects, religion, activities. And, over time, as we adapt to these comfort surrogates, especially as they become threatened or at risk of being taken away, we summon the need to defend. And we often do it unknowingly, as our beliefs, right or wrong, become entrenched. Disagreement is born, and we come to believe that our way of thinking is the better way. The like-minded form groups, and if you happen to go against the grain, well, you're not exercising any common sense.

Origins aside, the Black Lives Matter movement raises a complicated and heated issue, caught between what some perceive to be common sense and what others feel is right and just. For starters, take the slogan itself, "Black Lives Matter." It only works if you're in the know, and that "know" is apparently a big ask for some people. It requires a lot of information and understanding, even for those willing to listen who don't feel threatened by the prospect of change. For many, this phrase has an obvious meaning. But to the uninformed, those three words may simply be too much to grasp. Think about "Just do it." What's that supposed to mean to the non-athletically initiated? Do what? Anything that needs explanation, especially something as important as the Black Lives Matter movement as a moniker for social change, if not clearly spelled out and assimilated within the context of each of our lives, is a recipe for confusion and further division. And when people get called out as being the "idiot" for not understanding its "obvious" implications, the defenses go up, and the battle for who's right and who's wrong ensues. And what's really important, the substance of the issue gets obscured. And once again, the supposed binder of most of our beliefs, a gathering point for commonality, common sense, is nowhere in sight.

Some fall into the "all lives matter" semantics game, which is akin to the "You're a racist, but what am I" antagonistic retort wordplay we'd toss around as a five-year-old – further derailing the substance of the issue. But somewhere in there, I believe most of us want the same thing – the "less aware" are just too afraid to admit they don't have all the pieces (that whole entrenchment thing). So, I propose a new name for the movement: "Hey White-privileged dumbass – yeah, you! The constitution applies to African Americans and people of all races when it comes to treating our citizens equally, and here are examples of where this hasn't quite worked out so well. [Insert list: i.e., an officer kneeling on the neck of a defenseless Black man until he suffocates to death, the kid in the lunchroom who must steal food to eat, etc.]" It may be kind of long, even as an acronym, but it's an inarguable representation of what's really going on here. People deserve clarity; they need to be educated. Lose the slogans people.

Common Sense as I See It

Arguments may sway and even be right. But the way of life governed by laws artfully set by the politicians we elect to office is often unkind to many. Is it not enough to seek to shift the tides towards our true purpose? I've listed a few things identified as products of this behavior. Perpetrated by a "well-intentioned" need to protect a point of view, yet shored up by an often misguided, false sense of what we really need to thrive as a people:

Healthcare and education should be affordable and accessible to all our citizens.

Borders should be meticulously managed and citizenship available and accessible to all who qualify and are able and willing to contribute to the community.

All our leaders should have a demonstrable track record of providing service to our citizens before getting elected – show us you care because when people are involved, kindness matters.

Everyone in our country should have access to basic food made from the healthiest ingredients.

Semi-automatic rifles have no place in the general population

– go to a range to shoot them off.

Stop screwing with "daylight saving time" – keeping track of time is hard enough.

No one should be without a place to live. Each state should have acreage set aside on the periphery of more densely populated areas for sustainable, low-income, decent-quality housing. This should incorporate a tiered housing structure to accommodate family size and situation. To provide security, rehab, healthcare, job training, and jobs. To graduate most of its inhabitants back into society to be productive citizens. To protect those unable to fully contribute, support those who are sick, and incarcerate habitual offenders. It should be subsidized by the government and donors and supported by habitants and workers.

We can and should construct an economy that encompasses alternative energy to preserve the resources that we do have and minimize emissions. It doesn't take a scientist to point out that releasing tons of carcinogens into the atmosphere isn't helpful or healthy – all you have to do is fart in a tent to figure that one out. It doesn't have to happen overnight and would need to transition purposefully to prevent the economy from collapsing, but a plan would be helpful. Whatever the cause and origin of greenhouse gases, the result is the same and worth paying attention to.

Don't grab a knife by the sharp end.

Pleasant Memories:

The smell of fresh cut grass on a warm summer's day

Snuggling in bed with Grandma Doe on Christmas Eve

That excitement and energy leading up to Christmas morning

My wife's laugh when I say something goofy

Saturday mornings watching *Scooby Doo* with my mom

That other-worldly silence and resonant glow of freshly fallen snow

Most everything about being a kid

Packages under the tree

Summer nights and fireflies

My mother lightly scratching my head

The smell of turkey, pie, and rolls at Thanksgiving

Seeing my kids do well, and that look on their face when they know it

Playing kick-the-can

The ache in my legs as I went door-to-door once a year to collect candy

The glow, sound, and heat emanating from a crackling camp-fire

Liam rounding the corner, David knocking one in, Ruby caving an opponent's knees

That two-beer buzz

The not-so-sick days

Not-so-Pleasant Memories:

Getting caught looking at another student's paper

Biting down on a bad nut

Flashing lights in the rearview mirror

Taking the last swig only to find a cigarette butt at the bottom

Breaking my leg playing kick-the-can

Getting caught stealing a toy at the local dime store when I was seven

Letting my mom down for any reason

Not finding the right words

Chasing that two-beer buzz

Sick days

Wishes:

That I was a better student in school

That I could fly

That I could say the right things when my kids need it most

That running was easy for me

That we lived in a world with less pain

That I better understood why we live in a world with pain

That we had a clearer sense for what lies beyond

That I was smarter

Regrets:

Not loving fully sooner

Not giving of myself the way she deserves

That I was mean to anyone

That I was not at peace with my art

That I didn't read more when I was younger

Not being by her side when she passed

October 16, Year Five

A few months ago, I approached Dr. Simon to discuss turning over all the stones that may be causing the cognitive symptoms that I'm still experiencing. As part of my wellness plan, we agreed to a barrage of tests, including blood screenings, brain MRI, and urine analysis. I shifted towards a lower glycemic, gluten- and dairy-free diet. We discovered elevated levels of lead in my blood, which we addressed with aggressive, foods-based detoxification followed by Rx chelation. This initial step was an intense nine-week dietary program designed to optimize the stomach, liver, and kidneys. The second step was a fourteen-week cycle of chelation medication supported by supplements, a specific whole foods diet, and other physical detoxification methods, including frequent saunas, contrast showers, and continued exercise.

Despite all this, and being on a primarily whole foods diet the past five months, my cognitive state remains little changed. However, my sleep has improved slightly. Also, my blood pressure has dropped to a new low: 115/65. Inflammation in my body and aches and pains previously associated with exercise have dissipated. My recovery time after rigorous workouts have shortened. Despite initially feeling the effects of the lower-carb diet as a lack of energy in my legs, my running times have since improved to a ten-year best!

I would have expected to see measurable cognitive improvement by now but remain cautiously optimistic that noticeable improvements will happen a few cycles into the chelation process. It seems plausible that lead, a neurotoxin that has been in my system for decades, could be disruptive to my central nervous system, causing many of the cognitive anomalies I've been experiencing these past several years, accentuated or "unleashed" amid the alprazolam incident.

TWENTY-TWO

ON WELLNESS

To address an earlier question, I'm not sure how I continued working once the adverse effects of the medication had fully set in. Initially, it was a moment-by-moment assessment of what I could and couldn't do. Driven by a voice in my head that told me to keep plowing ahead – like my own private coxswain – which eventually led me down a path of self-discovery. A crusade of sorts, to learn and do everything I possibly could to find my way back to better health. A process that involved reaching out to others and educating myself about what I should put into my body and what to avoid. How I move, how I think … as well as confronting the societal impediments in pursuit of this mission. I was determined to undo the mistakes of the past and incorporate healthy habits going forward.

Consequently, over the past several years, I have learned a few things about wellness. And what it means to work towards healing and being healthy. First and foremost, it's a work in progress. There is no such thing as a quick fix, be that a pill or otherwise (I had to learn that the hard way). Wellness is achieved through a series of lifestyle adaptations comprised of a variety of activities. And conversely, not being well is more often associated with complacency and the many not-so-good choices we make. The most eye-opening revelation about all of this for me is how much power we have in managing our own health – through education, diet, exercise, and developing and maintaining a positive outlook on life.

I suspect that simply by becoming more aware of the fundamental needs of our own well-being and taking ownership, we'd rid our society of a preponderance of the disease that plagues us today. And by reprioritizing our healthcare system to embrace these preventative measures, we could save billions of dollars and millions of lives. But our system isn't incentivized to save billions. It's currently dependent upon the sick remaining sick to ensure those dollars continue to flow through the established channels and drive profits for big business. After all, we are a capitalistic society. However, I do think the tide is shifting, albeit painfully slowly.

Many of the problems I've faced were borne out of my own laziness and ignorance, coupled with the blind faith I placed in my doctor. I regret now that I chose to follow his recommendation to take a pharmaceutical approach rather than do the work necessary to pursue a path of natural healing – I mean, our bodies generally prefer to heal more naturally if given the opportunity.

My doctor's recommendation, the more conventional method, was to treat the symptom rather than the cause. This approach led to unnecessarily prescribed medications to address a relatively minor issue, leading to dependency, adversely affecting my psychological well-being. And, leaving me more reliant than ever on a one-size-fits-all system to try to rectify the damage that, in large measure, it had caused.

I soon realized that it would take more than modern medicine to get better. I needed to step outside of convention and adapt to a new way of living to repair the damage from within. Fortunately, more natural options for maintaining good health are becoming widely accepted and accessible to most everyone. A philosophy of treating your mind, body, and spirit "holistically" is often the first and best line of defense to prevent illness. And there is a substantial body of evidence to support this. It is just a matter of taking responsibility for your health and putting in the work. To help others, you must do you well first. The American dream needs to include the American wellness plan.

Many of the not-so-uncommon challenges that preceded my immediate health crisis occurred simply because of the sort of person I am – one of the more subdued, artistic, and empathetic types that make up a substantial part of the population. They've got a name for it, the "Highly Sensitive Person," or HSP. This isn't a bad thing, but it does present impediments, especially as we move through a world that is not necessarily kind to the fragile at heart. We are strong and resilient, but we have an Achilles heel. We are sensitive.

The most egregious of my sensitivities presented itself in an inability to drift off naturally and fall asleep within a reasonable amount of time. Everyone has their thing. However, rather than recognizing this as an opportunity to understand myself better, I went for the easy fix addressing the symptom instead of taking a broader look at how I was living my life. What better option than to desensitize my sensitivities with a quick-fix prescribed to me by my "trusted" doctor. Meanwhile, being told by another doctor that I had sleep apnea. A revelation that only heightened my anxieties around sleep and further hampered what little sleep I was getting, which was already grossly insufficient and inimical to my health.

Between pharmaceutically induced anxiety and other related anomalies – a lack of sleep, and now, apparently, "asphyxiation" during the night – I was slowly degrading the quality of my health and opening myself up to cardiovascular issues, if not an early death. In other words, under the care and direction of my physicians, I was slowly dying and reliant as ever on a costly industry to maintain a baseline quality of life. My two major health factors – sensitive sleeper and sleep apnea – conspired to make my life hell. And yet, on the bright side, ironically, set me on a path towards resetting my priorities.

Fortunately, I have been exercising and running for most of my life because I've always felt, deep down, that it's the right thing for me to do. I am otherwise a sedentary person by nature. My wife would qualify me as "the slowest walker on the planet." And yet, somehow, I'm able to summon the discipline necessary to extricate myself from the prone position. And, despite running for the past few decades, it has never come easily – it takes work most days. To make it fun, I draw inspiration from others. Sometimes I envision myself running amongst the best athletes in the world, cruising along at the front of the pack. Or I conjure up memories from my early cross-county days and imagine the chants of support I got from my coach as he would usher us through to the finish line when all I wanted to do was die. "You got this!! Let's Go!!! Give me two!!!!"

I run because I know something inside me needs this. Experiencing intense physical exertion helps me feel calm and rested. It would not be far-fetched to suggest that exercise has saved my life. It has certainly gotten me this far and served me well. It releases pent-up anxieties and helps flush out my brain and body with healthy blood flow and fresh oxygen. For me, it's running. For others, it may be a long walk, biking, swimming, or whatever else gets the heart rate going for any sustained period. Just do it™ – there's your context.

There have been too many times when the last thing I wanted to do was go for a run – my energy levels and motivation so low that it was all I could do to haul my ass off the couch and stand up. Toss in some cold rain and wind, aches and pains, and the thought of doing nothing is as enticing as a tray of freshly baked cookies. Nevertheless, I overcome, lace-up, and schlep my rear out the door. I exercise because I know once I start moving, things shift. The veil lifts, and my attitude changes. I feel energized and satisfied for having done something productive for my health. And that is one powerful prescription.

It's true, you are what you eat. Food and nutrients fuel our relationship with the world expressed through chemical reactions between our brain, organs, and muscles. Treating your body well from the inside out improves the odds of living well. Additionally, regulatory systems can be further enhanced by properly administered high-quality vitamins. However, the health supplement industry is complicated and unregulated, making finding the appropriate vitamins confusing and potentially risky. It is, therefore, beneficial to work with a knowledgeable naturopathic doctor and licensed dietitian to devise a plan to address your specific physiological needs.

Working with my naturopathic doctor was essential to reclaiming my health, calming my nerves, and optimizing my brain function. There was no way I could navigate the thousands of purported remedies available without expert care and advice. It would have been too daunting to discern the phony from the real, the quality from the crap, let alone know how best to administer the proper dosages. And having a general grasp of how the biochemical interactions worked helped me visualize the healing process. Supplements can be beneficial, but they require the utmost care to ensure a productive outcome.

I am not anti-medicine by any means. There are critical instances when a pharmaceutical approach is essential to the healing process, negating the effects of diseases and saving lives. There is no question that advances in medicine have resulted in miracle cures for millions and extended life for millions more. Nonetheless, I do believe that we are an over-medicated society propped up by an economically incentivized healthcare system with its priorities disproportionately biased towards corporate profits.

December 26, Year Six

I still attribute much of how I feel today to what happened with the alprazolam debacle several years ago. Maybe this is misplaced. Regardless, the symptomatic episodes have lessened. And yet, I'm still experiencing mental discomfort and anxiety fueled by fear. Fear that my cognitive faculties are eroding. That I may be sick, or something is permanently off. Hard to believe, after so many years, this could be so. At this point, I must find the strength to accept things as they are and move on. This is my new reality. I pray for the strength to persevere. I pray that one day I will feel whole once again.

My fears are the same old irrational thoughts. I wish I could have learned to let things go by now. But apparently, it's not that simple – with time, life keeps plowing ahead. That said, may I continue to grow, mature, and redirect my energy towards helping others rather than simply fixating on my own deficits.

About a third of the U.S. population takes a mental-anesthetizing prescription drug to help them get through the day. That's 100 million people, unable to fully cope, who have opted for pharmacological relief, despite the natural, arguably more effective options available. Again, many need this kind of treatment, but not all. Probably not even most. That is a lot of dependencies and just one example of the proliferation of a drug within a population. It comes down to profits over people, sorry to say. American healthcare is built on a culture that has yet to fully embrace the preemptive measures that would deter many of its citizens from requiring life-enhancing medications to begin with – for ailments that stretch the gamut. Once those dominoes start to fall, they are hard to stop.

I stumbled across mindfulness meditation about a month before stopping alprazolam altogether. I was feeling progressively worse and needed to act. I learned that this was something simple and proven I could start immediately. So, I attended a Mindfulness-Based Stress Reduction course to help ease my newfound anxiety, a side effect of the medication. Mindfulness creates space around every aspect of your being – allowing room to observe what you're experiencing from moment to moment – centered around your breathing and other sensations in the body. That's it. Nothing to it. Just twenty or so minutes a day to focus on being present, alert, and fully conscious.

The cumulative effect of incorporating this practice into my routine has been subtle yet transformative. And numerous studies have shown this to be the case for many. It has enabled me to understand that how and what I feel need not define who I am – disarming any negative thoughts (or delusional power trips) that I might be experiencing on a particular day. It also helps me remain grounded. And to be more aware of the effect I have on my relationships with others. It takes a while. I consider myself a dabbler, and yet I've been at it for more than six years and view mindfulness as an essential tool in the progression of my wellbeing. You can take a pill to mask how you feel temporarily, or you can take a few minutes each day to focus on your inner self. There is value in letting the pain in, observing it, and accepting things as they are.

Before World War II, the USDA instituted the concept of the "Basic Seven," dietary guidelines deemed essential to healthy eating. In addition to forming the starting point for what we thought of as the optimal American diet, a precursor to the food pyramid, it also established the framework for industrialized food production industries to take root and flourish. Such as dairy – one of those core staples once identified as fundamental to our diet – sell lots of milk and cheese you and the economy will benefit mightily. But as we've learned, dairy is not as healthy as once thought and, as a result, consumption has slowly declined ever since. (It should be noted that cheese and ice cream are among my personal favorites.) Adjacent to dairy, we had meat, also once deemed essential, now relegated to a much broader category called "proteins," which includes all kinds of healthier options and plant-based alternatives, many of which have absolutely nothing to do with meat (or dairy).

We also have the industries responsible for making food look plump long enough to make it to our tables. The pioneers in the development of hormone injections and modified feed, a plethora of insecticides, and genetically modified organisms, along with a variety of chemical preservation techniques to enhance longevity. Meanwhile, concurrently (and not so coincidentally), over the past few generations, we've seen an uptick in common illnesses such as obesity, heart disease, and diabetes, coupled with a fantastic array of expensive medicines and treatments to counteract these ailments. One can't help but connect the dots.

Celiac tendencies or not, our processed wheat flour has an inflammatory effect at a cellular level for all of us, with varying outcomes and reactions – joint pain, stomach ailments, clouded thinking, and susceptibility to colds, among others. Milk and dairy products disrupt the gut, block nutrients, and cause irritation to the digestive tract. Granulated sugars and sugar alternatives inflame the cells and wreak havoc on other critical systems. The further we stray from fresh whole foods, the more damage we inflict on our bodies. Over time, the industrial food complex's microscopic toxins and other carcinogens build up in our cells and begin to have a corrosive, inflammatory effect, weakening our natural defenses against autoimmune enemies such as viruses, cancers, and other diseases.

Much of what we put into our bodies is the product of an ill-conceived, economy-first, food production system, intended to fill our stomachs for the lowest cost possible with minimal consideration of our long-term health. Much of our food today is produced with a litany of chemicals and environmental toxins. Due in large to the build-up of pollutants in our groundwater, soil, and air. The cumulative effects of which, when ingested, conspire to lower our bodies' natural defenses and immunities. Sure, the food system has kept us alive, but it has also made us even more susceptible to disease and a variety of other ailments, prematurely. Consequently, it has spawned an industry of consumers seeking immediate relief from a wide range of illnesses such as heartburn, headaches, and inflammation, not to mention numerous other afflictions like the need (as in my case) for better sleep.

Fortunately, the realities about diet and food production processes continue to evolve. We have finally arrived at a time when awareness of what we eat and how it gets produced are beginning to tip the scales to benefit the consumer. As a result, and thanks to the proliferation of organic farms and local farmers' markets and improved production standards, the quality of our food has improved significantly. And, as we become ever more enlightened to these truths, systemic and sweeping change will eventually find its way into everybody's home, regardless of income or status. We are becoming the experts. But much work remains.

Up to this point, my association with 'beets' had been limited to David's affinity for hip-hop music, a couple of interludes with Country Dick Montana, and a few casual encounters at the dinner table. But to rid my body of the accumulation of crud I had picked up over the years meant I'd have to get a whole lot more intimate with this vegetable – to the extent of grotesque nausea. The kidney-cleansing regimen seemed like an eternity but lasted only ten days. Ten days of thick, unsweetened pure beet mush and the after-burn that followed. Sure, it was a little nasty going down, but a highly effective way to recharge my kidneys and cure my gut of any maladies - which, by extension, improved pathways to the brain. Detoxing the system was the first step towards resetting my digestive tract. And I haven't had an upset stomach since.

Eight years ago, my initial two-night sleep study at the Polyclinic determined that I was waking about thirty times per hour. The recommendation was to use a CPAP machine, the "gold standard" for treatment. I subsequently ran out and bought a top-of-the-line device with all the bells and whistles and began to incorporate it into my sleep routine. I was optimistic, knowing that finally addressing sleep would help my energy levels improve. But despite my determination, I was unable to tolerate the device, which led to further disruption in sleep. I tried all kinds of alternative approaches: mouth guards, head straps, propping pillows under my chin – short of following up on my doctor's off-hand, marginally snarky remark, "I've heard of a guy who plays the didgeridoo who claims he no longer has sleep apnea."

As part of a more recent plan to approach my healing journey more holistically, I once again revisited my sleep issue. But this time, I went to Harborview Medical Center and met with their sleep doctor. I informed her of my situation and that I was once again open to trying anything. And, that I was skeptical of whether I had sleep apnea at all. Aside from the cloudy head and fatigue that I regularly felt, much of which I attributed to the benzos aftermath, I just wasn't displaying the hallmark symptoms of the condition. She'd hear nothing of it and insisted that the initial data gathered eight years prior was still valid. "You don't just 'get over it,'" she said and recommended that I once again revert to that "gold standard," the dreaded CPAP.

This time around, after years of mindfulness practice, I tolerated the device. Meanwhile, upon asking about alternative therapies and getting a nearly identical response as the previous doctor, I took it upon myself to purchase a didgeridoo and learned to play it. Several months passed, and although my CPAP data showed that my "episodes" reduced consistently to the realm of "healthy" (two episodes per hour, down from thirty), she attributed the readings as evidence that the device was working. However, at this point, I didn't believe that I had sleep apnea. If I had sleep apnea, I'd be snoring or waking more – and the treatment, from my perspective, was having no perceptible effect on my health. She explained this lack of "overt" relief as having something to do with a potentially mysterious type of sleep apnea – even more ambiguity. "I'm doomed," I thought.

Her disinclination to listen and her reluctance to retest prompted me to initiate a sleep test with my dentist. A three-night process that recorded my brain waves, heart vitals, and breathing – measuring any type of sleep apnea-related events. If anything, this was a more comprehensive test than the one performed several years earlier, and without the aid of a benzo to help me fall asleep (or a CPAP machine). Analysis by a third-party sleep specialist determined that I was experiencing fewer than two events per hour – the lower end of the "normal" threshold. A similar reading compared to the data shown on the CPAP device I had been using for the better part of a year. In other words, I did not have sleep apnea. Translation – I am that guy who has been cured by mastering the didgeridoo. Sleep apnea was curable for me (or I never had it in the first place, and it was benzo-induced respiratory suppression). And it seems reasonable that it could be for many others as well. I understand some people need the device to retain proper oxygen levels in their blood. It has its place. But it is also apparent that the sleep medicine industry is not particularly interested in helping you become well. They only want to treat the symptoms. That's how they get paid.

To any "sleep docs" reading this, please don't offer sensitive sleepers the "gold standard" as the primary and most effective solution for treating sleep apnea. The reason 80 percent of patients go untreated is that the treatments offered are too invasive and not conducive to helping them fall and stay asleep. And many of us are HSPs. You make a living off those few who can tolerate the device and the revolving door of those who seek help, knowing damn well they won't be able to sustain the treatment long term. Your mission as a "sleep specialist" should be to treat the remaining 80 percent effectively. Your current approach is anything but a gold standard. I can only imagine the number of devices collecting dust under beds (I have two) and the thousands of dollars wasted in pursuit of a cure (you're welcome). Viable alternatives exist for many patients who do not require anxiety-inducing treatments such as the CPAP or the adverse effects of potentially harmful prescription drugs. And, once the healthcare system becomes incentivized to address and treat the cause rather than the symptom, these alternatives will become more widely available. But you may also be out of a job, and millions of people's quality of life will improve.

Friendships require attention. At the onset of the healing process, it was all I could do to make it to the end of each day and rally against the tendency to isolate myself. As time progressed, I realized I was missing opportunities to form new friendships and tending less to existing ones. It was hard but necessary to push myself to make these connections and confront and overcome any discomfort and fear I may have had to remain active and engaged. Again – fake it until you make it.

I was a self-assured, stubborn renegade, and the thought of counseling for any reason never entered my mind – head down, go it alone. Then came my forties. At which point, as with many couples, Camille and I agreed that marital mediation would benefit both of us. And it did. This experience taught me the value of having an outside voice to help facilitate communication between two people – it enabled me to better understand how to interpret the feelings and reactions of others. And it also made it easier for me to shed the stigma that I had affixed to counseling and recognize that maybe I didn't have things as buttoned-up as I liked to think.

There was a time when the support I was receiving from my therapist was essential – to see me through the week. I've sought his advice and guidance on many topics as I navigate around the complexities of raising a family and the uncertainties surrounding the healing process. I am indebted to Eric, and his capacity to listen despite having to put up with my relentless recounting of events. But he was the light that I needed during a difficult time. And I am grateful for the advice, wisdom, and validation he has seeded along the way.

I was very fortunate to retain my job throughout this health-related ordeal, although it was all I could do to not tap out. Mindfulness and the support of family and friends helped me move forward, retain perspective, and thus stay employed. And the benefits of staying employed far exceeded collecting a paycheck. Being at the office and engaging with coworkers was exhausting but also mentally stimulating. I also endeavored to keep my mind active with Sudoku puzzles, participating in card games, and learning to juggle little round balls. And I guess I have taken up writing too.

I am also preparing myself for a potential career change. I've been practicing those interview questions and figuring out how best to present myself when a job opportunity does arise. And making plans for if and when I do become inspired to once again cut out on my own. It's time to dust off the resume update the portfolio (careful not to include too much of my art), and prepare myself for that next endeavor. A little preparation will go a long way to boost my confidence and reduce that feeling of helplessness when things are changing by the moment.

September 10, Year Six

As I think about this last journal entry, it has been a long time coming. I remember looking ahead to a day when the symptoms no longer consume me. That is when I would consider myself healed. Although I'm not exactly where I want to be, I do think I've met that criterion. Is what I'm feeling today, remnants of brain fog, fuzzy memory, lack of confidence, and poor sleep tied to those events six years ago? It's hard to say. And it doesn't matter at this point – it is what it is. Ten years from now, I'll look back on all this and know a lot more than I do today. If I feel better, enough said, it was just a passing, difficult period in my life. If the same, that's OK too, because I will have learned to adapt. If, however, it proves to be something that slowly consumes me over time, well, this record of my experience may offer some insights into the cause for anyone who cares to understand. Regardless, I will continue to live my best life and seek activities that benefit my well-being. Whatever the outcome, I'll know I gave everything to make the best of a challenging and prolonged situation.

But, for today, and on this topic, it's time to move on.

EPILOGUE

Our stories differ widely; no two are the same. Mine is of my own making. And though it may not seem particularly interesting to some, I celebrate the path I chose, which has led me to the person I am today, for better and for worse.

Like having a backup generator in the ready, people take comfort in different things. Some rely on family and friends, faith or religion, or their own inherent well of resilience. But whatever fuels us, whatever we're open to, it is reassuring to know that hope knows no shape. It's up to us to keep an open mind and allow it to flow into our lives.

I've drawn strength from various sources – an amalgam of my own life experiences. The hardships I experienced relocating from Chicago to New Jersey during an impressionable period in my life before finally arriving in the Northwest to start anew with family. The lessons I learned from being raised by well-intentioned and loving parents. Fumbling my way through adolescence and young adulthood lived and experienced through the prism of heightened sensitivities. The wicked hangover, which could just as easily have resulted in my own professional Armageddon, would ironically become my guiding light as I faced my most challenging personal trial to date. And I revel in those odds of choosing that Christmas party over Gilligan, ending up on that kitchen floor, and finding a partner to share and experience the blessings life has to offer. In all its glorious heartache.

Camille and I talk about the five-year plan often. If all goes well, Liam will have graduated from Western Washington University, and David will be right in the middle of his schooling at Saint Martin's. Ruby will have graduated high school and be preparing to head off to college to continue her education and play soccer. At which point we may sell the house and relocate to a less expensive part of the state, or maybe out of state – who knows? A smaller town with fewer big-city distractions, less traffic, and a renewed sense of community. These past few years have been a grind. It is time for a change.

We plan to cash in on our hard-earned equity and move to a place that needs little repair – a turnkey home, maybe with a pool and a few acres. Given the current state of the economy and where things are headed, it shouldn't be too hard to find twice the house for half the price in a community that isn't so financially demanding. We'd also like to buy an RV and experience domestic travel with a little less chaos. To have the means and freedom to visit the kids and friends wherever they may be and hit the road more often. And to see other parts of the world. We hope to bankroll this with part-time, less taxing jobs and begin to tap into some of the investments we've made over the years.

It's hard to believe that we're nearing that stage in life in which we'll be living without kids – as empty nesters. Fortunately, Camille and I like each other and enjoy spending time doing similar things. We'll miss our kids dearly and hope they will continue to occupy a significant part of our life. But we welcome this change and the freedom to live to our own agenda once again. To sleep in and eat out more often, know what's in the fridge, and have less laundry to do. To have more time for ourselves to do what we want, when we want, and to also give back to the community more regularly. There will be an adjustment period: getting used to the quiet, the echo of footsteps in place of the laughter, the yelling, the attitudes; no more balls bouncing off the walls and into the furniture; a break from worrying whether they'll make it home, or if we'll get that call; not being called on as much, because we are no longer needed. But I think we'll both look back on this time with satisfaction. That we showed up, participated, and gave it our all.

We do remain in a state of uncertainty. Not just for ourselves, but as a nation. The pandemic is still ablaze, and we're not quite sure what mid-to-long-term effect this will have on our lives, the world, and the economy. My current job is teetering on a thread, although I'm happy to report that I'm still employed. I was furloughed without pay for a while, as was Camille, and we both took a pay reduction for several months. The government stimulus payments were a lifeline that kept us from dipping too heavily into our savings. We refinanced the house to free up cash to help the boys through school and pay down debt. I'm still not sure if this will be enough. But if I've learned anything these past several years, it's that you can't control the future. We can only hope, plan, and pray for the best.

On the very bright side, Ruby has gotten a few full-ride scholarship offers from D1 programs despite most of her soccer season being canceled because of Covid. This is a blessing for all of us. She's worked hard for this moment; Camille and I look forward to watching her grow and mature as a player and a person. David is excited to begin school in the fall, and Saint Martin's is small enough to accommodate students safely despite the virus. He will have most of his expenses paid for as the result of combined soccer and academic scholarship. And should do well in an environment that invests heavily in getting to know their students, with a mission to support them in any way possible.

Liam has had a challenging year. He went through a tough breakup with his girlfriend and changed his academic focus due to the last-minute dissolution of the major he was planning to pursue (automotive engineering). And, of course, the virus has impacted his personal and work life as well. But we think he has finally had a chance to reset his compass and figure a few things out. And, with the school money Camille's parents set aside years ago, coupled with the scholarship support from the other two, we are optimistic that we will be able to get him through school with minimal student debt as well. We have been fortunate that all three kids have worked very hard to make the most of their opportunities.

When times are challenging, I tend to take on lofty (and often silly) goals to provide extra incentive behind whatever I happen to be taking on – personal challenges to push myself outside of my comfort zone. I adopt a kind of "fight fire with fire" mentality. I find that setting and meeting these goals brings its own reward, especially during times of uncertainty. This past year, with anxiety around work, the financial hurdles, Covid, and navigating around my health, these extra incentives helped me stay on track.

I started things off last summer with three attempts to run around Lake Washington. A fifty-mile route connected by trails, streets, and neighborhoods. It's a beautiful trek that takes you through several parks and a few cities, affording pristine and relaxing views of the shoreline. I say "attempts" because I have yet to make it all the way around fully. But even though I've come up short (forty-two miles my best), I enjoyed the challenge and look forward to the possibility of one day completing the loop.

During the spring 2021 pandemic lockdown, I was denied my regular workout routine at the nearby athletic field. So, I traded in discouragement for an over-the-top challenge to do ten thousand pull-ups in ten weeks. I completed the feat in my backyard and followed up with one thousand pull-ups one morning a week later. And forty consecutive pull-ups the week after that. A display of braggadocio, maybe, but I can think of many less productive activities with which to fill my time. Hey, whatever it takes. My juggling continues to improve, and I look forward to wrapping up this book soon, to be capped off with a bonfire and a ceremonious burning of its pages.

Is it critical that I express myself more fully as a visual artist one day? I don't know. I've had a taste over the years, exhibiting at a few cafés and bars (fig. 40, p. 192), and yet the stars haven't fully aligned. I hope that when I revisit my creative side, I do so with the right mindset, for the right reasons, let my expectations fall to the wayside, and simply enjoy the act of doing. It would be fun to experiment with painting again. To put down on canvas what only I can express. Once we get out from under the rigors of running the household, the demands of work, and have a bit more time for ourselves to pursue the things we want, maybe I'll have the space to reenergize this aspect of myself.

When things go sideways – and life gets crazy, I believe there remains a capacity to go un-sideways as well. There are untapped resources inherent to everyone. And yet, it is up to each to seek out our path towards wellness and healing and cultivate self-awareness.

Unfortunately, there's too much emphasis on medicine as the fallback to make life tolerable, rather than buckle down and do the work necessary to heal. The pharmaceutical industry all too readily promotes remedies that more often mask the clues our bodies send us, covering up the signals that our way of living and looking at the world may have gotten off course somehow. And it's not too difficult to see how this came to be, in a culture that brought us Burger King and taught us that money, winning, and instant gratification reign above all else.

We are constantly distracted from living a life of higher purpose. We've been reared within a culture of skin-deep values, intolerant of what's truly best for each of us. And one day, amidst the uncertainty, we may be called on to look inward, to contemplate our place in this world. To try and make sense of things. And with that invitation, I see an opportunity to pull back the blinds and contemplate life's meaning – to be kind and loving to those around me. And to reflect and be accountable for what I've become. To be courageous and pursue a path of self-discovery. To one day feel at home in the house I built.

Starting at the top, from left to right

1. Scott and Kent welcoming me into this world.
2. A family portrait in Western Springs, 1974.
3. My first art show.
4. Mom tending to a bump.
5. Dad on the move with his camera.
6. Another night in that musty canvas tent.
7. Gearing up for an outing with my fellow 'guides'.
8. Still taller than the rest, despite my broken leg.

9. *Sledding in our backyard in Montclair New Jersey.*
10. *Playing smear the queer in the backyard.*
11. *That's me in the foreground - slow off the blocks.*
12. *Kent and I working on the Falcon.*
13. *There's a human under that shaving cream.*
14. *On my way back from Chicago.*
15. *The painting at the foot of the bed.*
16. *A rare quiet moment with Stephen.*

17. *King Richard's Faire - Stephen's face poking through the middle.*
18. *Finishing my first marathon in the cold November rain, 1987.*
19. *Mom (center) being a good host at a DesignSight party.*
20. *Camille and Chris living carefree.*
21. *Efim at his home in Moscow with his aunt and uncle.*
22. *Being kept awake by the aging tracks - somewhere west of Moscow.*
23. *A new chapter.*
24. *Momma with her brood.*

25. Parades are a small town tradition - Liam and David, Brentford SD.
26. A camping stopover en route to Turton.
27. A view of Turton.
28. Irvin Troske, out standing in his field.
29. Dakota.
30. An early treehouse in the greenbelt behind our home in Lake Forest Park.
31. Our humble abode in Wedgwood.
32. Digging out the basement, one bucket at a time.

33. *Getting ready to lay down the tar paper.*
34. *Kyle's ghost bike memorial, chained to a utility pole just down the street.*
35. *Taking a break with the kids.*
36. *Ruby and Lughano getting in their training.*
37. *David on the pitch.*
38. *Liam - bright-eyed and bushy-tailed, hour one.*
39. *Liam leading the pack in the 800.*
40. *A recent art show of my paintings at a local cafe.*

Photo Credits:

1-4, 7-12, 16-19, 30, 37-38 by Gary Settle
Cover, 26-29, 31-33, 35 by Camille Settle
13-14, 20-22, 24-25, 34, 40 by Chris Settle
5-6, 15 by Patti Settle
23 by Natalie Fobes
36 by Dean Rutz / The Seattle Times
39 by Kevin Lynch

Acknowledgments

Thank you to my care providers who cared enough to care: Dr. Simon and her relentless pursuit of an optimal wellness plan; Eric, my counselor throughout, for lending an ear and providing the emotional support I desperately needed to keep it together during a very trying time; and Gretchen for her nutritional guidance and expertise. A shout-out goes to David Bamford for helping bring shape to this book and keeping my grammar in check. Thanks to all my friends for the experiences we shared. To those who are no longer with us, to my mom and dad, who raised me well; and to my children, who've been the spark behind why I get up and do what I do every day. And a special thank you to my wife, Camille, for putting up with me, especially these past few years – they haven't been easy – and for allowing time for me to try and make sense of all this.

About the Author

Chris Settle is a self-described average guy with a less than stellar understanding of how the writing process works, which he's not ashamed to say is likely reflected in this work. That's not an apology. That's just how it is. Nevertheless, he stuck it out to produce a finished piece, which, he implores, "hopefully has some semblance to a coherent story." On a good day, this project would have been a challenge. But given the very real thought that perhaps this was his "time," he felt compelled to tell his story before too much more of life passed. Chris currently lives in Seattle with his wife and three children.

Made in the USA
Las Vegas, NV
24 January 2022

42233248R00115